MINDFULNESS
PUZZLES

MORE THAN 100 PUZZLES

ARCTURUS

ARCTURUS

This edition published in 2021 by Arcturus Publishing Limited
26/27 Bickels Yard, 151–153 Bermondsey Street,
London SE1 3HA

ISBN: 978-1-83857-742-1
AD007909NT

Printed in China

CONTENTS

Introduction

"Take care of this moment."

Gandhi

Mindfulness asks little from us, only that we take care of this moment. It's surprising how hard that can be.

In a world that is angry and fractured, where the news feed on our phones brings even more reasons for anger, this moment easily becomes a place where we feel trapped.

That trap, though, is our own. Marcus Aurelius explained this best: "You have power over your mind—not outside events. Realize this, and you will find strength."

So take a moment for yourself. Focus on here, focus on now. Yesterday is behind you, tomorrow will unfold at its own pace. Let mindfulness bring you back to today. To this moment, now.

That's all mindfulness means. And it's a practice that can be easily developed. There's no need for yoga classes or learning to meditate. You can simply solve a puzzle.

A puzzle is a problem with a solution, one that you will certainly find. Every puzzle in this book has easy-to-follow instructions and all the information you need to make an attempt.

The puzzles are of various types. Some you may recognize; others may be unfamiliar. You may find yourself trying one approach, then realizing it doesn't work and reaching for another. The point is, the puzzle is here and now—and so are you.

Don't let yourself believe this is a waste of your time. Self-indulgent even. Mindfulness is not self-indulgent. Mindfulness is looking after yourself. Studies have shown that the ability to focus on the present, and on what you can do, enhances well-being and reduces stress. In turn, this boosts creativity and undermines self-doubt.

It is when we leave self-doubt behind that we are able to see the truth of another insight from Marcus Aurelius: "Everything we hear is an opinion, not a fact. Everything we see is a perspective, not the truth."

Remember that, and it's easier to reject anger and to discover what it is you really think.

We hope that these puzzles help you relax, show you how to cultivate mindfulness—and lead the way back to yourself.

"Sometimes the most important thing in a whole day is the rest we take between two deep breaths."

Etty Hillesum

1   **Maze**

Start at the top and find a path to the middle of the maze.

"Silence is the great teacher,
and to learn its lessons you
must pay attention to it. There
is no substitute for the creative
inspiration, knowledge, and stability
that come from knowing how to
contact your core of inner silence."

Deepak Chopra

2　Wordsearch: Islands of the Pacific

Can you find all of the listed words hidden in the grid below?
Words run horizontally, vertically or diagonally, in either a forward or
backward direction.

```
P A P K A O P A P A T B W D E
U U C L J A R V N P E N U M G
I H V L I N I K I B R C I A I
T K S E V L A L L G I D O L G
A P E N R H Y N A E S R E D F
M V A N O T B P H U A E D E R
I S R E J H A E K I H A M N O
T A I R U A S S A N E C K E R
I H R L A B O T S I R C N A S
R O E V L K E I S R I A U Z I
I W T J I A O F A R I P N H V
K L S C N H W T H A W A I I R
O A A W E N C A S W S N V G A
B N E W C A L E D O N I A H J
B D S M U R U R O A V U K G W
```

BIKINI

DUCIE

EASTER

FLINT

HAWAII

HONSHU

HOWLAND

JARVIS

KAOPAPA

KIRITIMATI

MAHIKEA

MALDEN

MURUROA

NASSAU

NECKER

NEW
　　CALEDONIA

NUNIVAK

PENRHYN

RAIATEA

RENNELL

SAKHALIN

SAN
　　CRISTOBAL

VOSTOK

WALLIS

3   Patchwork

Every square should be filled with a letter from A to E, and each heavily outlined set of five squares should contain five different letters. Every row and column must contain two of each letter.

Squares that share a common border may not contain the same letter.

		D			D	B		B	A
	E		D	A					
	D			E	C				
A			A	B					
	A				B		E		B
	C		A			E	D		
E		C							
C		D			D		B	C	
			E			E			D
	B	E						D	C

"Truth is a deep kindness
that teaches us to be
content in our everyday life
and share with the people
the same happiness."

Kahlil Gibran

Sudoku

Place one of the numbers from 1 to 9 into every empty cell so that each row, each column and each 3x3 block contains all the numbers from 1 to 9.

9			6		3			2
		5				8		1
	4	7		2	1			6
				1	4	6	8	
	3		5		6		9	
	6	2	3	7				
2			7	9		3	4	
4		8				7		
5			4		8			9

"Don't let yesterday use up too much of today."

Cherokee proverb

5   Codeword

Every letter in this puzzle has been replaced by a number, the number remaining the same for that letter wherever it occurs. Every letter of the alphabet has been used. Substitute numbers for letters to complete the codeword.

It may help to cross off the letters beneath the grid to keep a track of progress, and to use the reference box showing which numbers have been decoded. Three letters have already been entered into the grid, to help you on your way.

3	24	10	9	24	10	10	■	5	7	23	1	1	23
21	■	22	■	3	■	6	24	21	7	■	4	■	3
6	21	23	16	21	■	7	■	24	■	11	■	■	21
4	■	6	■	8	11	19	9	■	8	23	20	12	24	8
23	6 **L**	21	19	4	■	20	21	6	4	■	21	■	11
■	11 **O**	■	24	■	8	■	21	■	14	■	24
23	4 **T**	4	24	22	■	17	7	10	4	24	2	24	21	3
10	■	23	■	23	■	23	■	24	■	8	■	8	■	23
10	7	8	2	6	11	18	21	19	■	16	24	1	24	6
21	■	12	■	7	■	23	■	24	■	8
10	■	21	■	4	21	10	4	■	10	9	11	12	21
10	13	19	24	9	20	■	14	21	4	24	■	15	■	16
24	■	3	■	11	■	20	■	25	23	24	26	21
8	■	11	■	10	23	9	21	■	6	■	3	■	19
1	24	9	6	21	4	■	21	6	21	9	21	8	4

A B C D E F G H I J K L M
N O P Q R S T U V W X Y Z

1	2	3	4 **T**	5	6 **L**	7	8	9	10	11 **O**	12	13
14	15	16	17	18	19	20	21	22	23	24	25	26

6   Domino Placement

A standard set of 28 dominoes has been laid out as shown. Can you draw in the edges of them all?

The check-box is provided as an aid, so that you can see which dominoes have been located.

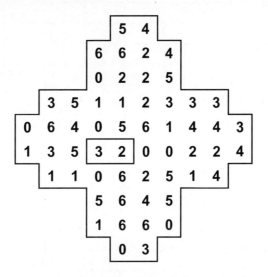

0-0	0-1	0-2	0-3	0-4	0-5	0-6	1-1	1-2	1-3	1-4	1-5	1-6	2-2

2-3	2-4	2-5	2-6	3-3	3-4	3-5	3-6	4-4	4-5	4-6	5-5	5-6	6-6
✓													

"Forever is composed of nows."

Emily Dickinson

Criss Cross: "SNOW..."

The words are provided, but can you fit them all into the grid?

3 letters	5 letters	6 letters
CAT	BLIND	BOARDS
MEN	BOOTS	CANNON
	BOUND	CAPPED
4 letters	FENCE	FLURRY
BELT	FIELD	MOBILE
CONE	GLOBE	ORCHID
DROP	GOOSE	
FALL	SCAPE	**7 letters**
LINE	SHOES	COVERED
MELT	SLIDE	LEOPARD
SUIT	STORM	MACHINE
	UNDER	

8   Wordsearch: A Walk in the Woods

Can you find all of the listed words hidden in the grid below? Words run horizontally, vertically or diagonally, in either a forward or backward direction.

```
Z  B  M  B  B  U  W  U  H  V  E  R  N  H  G
S  E  V  A  E  L  O  Q  V  N  E  A  B  B  G
N  E  V  X  P  I  R  T  O  E  E  B  I  E  D
D  A  L  K  S  L  C  D  D  F  A  H  R  R  H
E  Z  D  T  T  X  E  Y  P  O  N  A  C  R  E
A  L  H  W  T  Y  J  B  Y  L  L  O  H  I  M
L  E  I  F  R  E  R  X  B  I  Y  Q  C  E  L
P  G  J  H  U  A  N  E  W  A  E  M  E  S  O
S  V  Z  S  N  B  L  O  N  G  S  U  E  B  C
I  I  Q  C  K  T  L  S  A  E  W  S  B  A  K
X  A  H  K  E  L  T  E  S  O  E  H  H  D  W
S  E  U  E  I  R  A  S  C  S  S  R  D  G  T
S  W  B  W  E  P  O  Y  S  I  E  O  G  E  R
C  F  F  A  V  M  U  S  D  L  C  O  G  R  A
X  O  M  S  H  T  A  P  R  A  S  M  K  C  Q
```

BADGER	DEER	MOSSES
BEECH	FOLIAGE	MUSHROOM
BEETLE	GREENERY	NETTLES
BERRIES	HEMLOCK	PATHS
BIRCH	HOLLY	STREAM
BRANCHES	LEAVES	TRUNK
CANOPY	LICHEN	TWIGS
CROW	MAPLE	WILLOW

Number Link

Working from one square to another, horizontally or vertically (never diagonally), draw single continuous paths to pair up each set of two matching numbers.

No line may cross another, none may travel through any square containing a number, and every square must be visited just once.

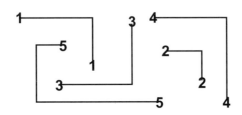

							11
10	2		8	3	4	8	
2			3				
6				10	9	4	
7		5					
				1			7
	6	5		9	1	11	

"Do not encumber your mind
with useless thoughts. What
good does it do to brood on
the past or anticipate the
future? Remain in the simplicity
of the present moment."

Dilgo Khyentse Rinpoche

10   Pyragram

Every clue in this puzzle is an anagram leading to a single-word solution. Correctly solve the anagram on each level of the pyramid and another word will appear, reading down the central column.

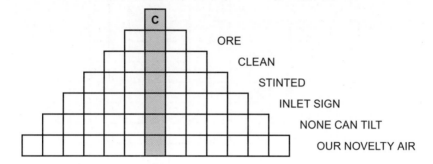

ORE

CLEAN

STINTED

INLET SIGN

NONE CAN TILT

OUR NOVELTY AIR

11   Word Wheel

How many words of three or more letters can you make from those in the wheel, without using plurals, abbreviations or proper nouns?

The central letter must appear once in every word and no letter in a section of the wheel may be used more than once.

There is at least one nine-letter word in the wheel.

Nine-letter word(s):

_____

12 Criss Cross: Lights

The words are provided, but can you fit them all into the grid?

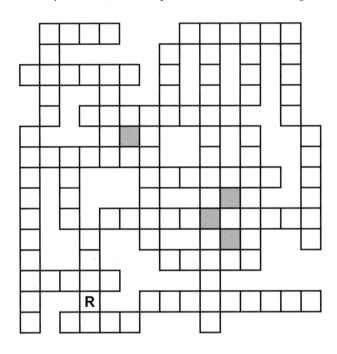

4 letters	MATCH	LANTERN
BEAM	TAPER	VOLTAGE
GLOW	TORCH	
MOON	WATTS	**8 letters**
NEON		DAYBREAK
STAR	**6 letters**	
	AURORA	**9 letters**
5 letters	BRIGHT	REFRACTED
BLAZE	STROBE	SPOTLIGHT
FLAME		
FLARE	**7 letters**	**10 letters**
GLEAM	BONFIRE	FLOODLIGHT
LASER	FIREFLY	

Sudoku

Place one of the numbers from 1 to 9 into every empty cell so that each row, each column and each 3x3 block contains all the numbers from 1 to 9.

8	7		5			3		
	9	4		6	7	5		
	6		2					9
	5			2		1		6
2			7		5			4
9		7		4			3	
7					1		8	
		3	6	8		9	1	
		1			9		5	2

"Every moment and
every event of every
man's life on earth plants
something in his soul."

Thomas Merton

14   Codeword

Every letter in this puzzle has been replaced by a number, the number remaining the same for that letter wherever it occurs. Every letter of the alphabet has been used. Substitute numbers for letters to complete the codeword.

It may help to cross off the letters beneath the grid to keep a track of progress, and to use the reference box showing which numbers have been decoded. Three letters have already been entered into the grid, to help you on your way.

8		15		24	26	5	8	17	8	26	5	8	26	16
20	8	26	11	26		3			10		25		15	
16		23		24	26	16	8	19	9	19	8	8	5	2
19	11	11	2	16		8			8		13		21	
11		26		24		5	19	24	14	14	13	24	8	19
7		1	15	3	6		24		14			26		8
8	10	15		16			2		13		9	8	3	15
19		8		8	26	22	11	6	8	5		20		17
16	15	19	4		3		16			8		3	2	12
8		8		2		16		8	17	24	23		11	
5	8	5	15	23	16	24(I)	11(O)	26(N)		11		16		13
	7		13		24		6		19	15	26	21	2	
23	11	15	26	16	8	19	17	13	11	16		8		16
	18		3		2		11		8	26	2	15	8	
16	8	3	19	2	16	3	24	26	8	5		2		19

A B C D E F G H I J K L M

N O P Q R S T U V W X Y Z

1	2	3	4	5	6	7	8	9	10	11 O	12	13
14	15	16	17	18	19	20	21	22	23	24 I	25	26 N

18

Wordsearch: Writing

Can you find all of the listed words hidden in the grid below?
Words run horizontally, vertically or diagonally, in either a forward or
backward direction.

```
C  L  A  N  O  I  T  A  M  R  I  F  N  O  C
N  E  R  I  M  T  P  I  E  C  E  R  N  P  N
I  T  A  L  I  C  S  H  S  D  A  M  D  E  E
G  N  I  D  A  E  R  S  O  M  E  M  T  N  T
I  N  V  O  I  C  E  R  E  T  L  B  P  E  T
G  O  A  C  Y  R  F  D  I  F  O  E  I  R  I
R  L  U  J  D  U  E  N  R  S  H  C  T  S  R
A  O  H  D  T  N  R  A  E  A  R  N  O  A  W
M  C  A  B  S  D  E  H  T  P  C  A  S  P  Q
M  I  N  U  T  E  N  T  L  E  T  T  E  R  Y
A  M  L  V  E  R  C  R  A  M  A  P  S  D  T
R  E  Y  E  Y  L  E  O  P  M  I  E  A  O  O
H  S  S  G  E  I  G  H  P  E  N  C  I  L  P
M  A  I  L  I  N  G  S  A  T  I  C  E  N  A
D  E  L  Y  R  E  V  I  L  E  D  A  R  M  S
```

ACCEPTANCE	LETTER	READING
ADDRESS	MAILING	RECEIPT
CONFIRMATION	MEMOS	REFERENCE
DEAR SIR	MINUTE	SEMICOLON
DELIVERY	OPENER	SHORTHAND
GRAMMAR	PENCIL	STAMPS
INVOICE	PHOTOCOPY	UNDERLINE
ITALICS	POSTCARD	WRITTEN

Criss Cross: On Vacation

The words are provided, but can you fit them all into the grid?

4 letters

AWAY

MAPS

TAXI

5 letters

CABIN

GROUP

GUIDE

HOTEL

VIEWS

6 letters

BIKINI

CAMERA

OUTING

VOYAGE

7 letters

AIRPORT

DAY TRIP

JOURNEY

TOURIST

VISITOR

8 letters

PASSPORT

POSTCARD

SUITCASE

9 letters

APARTMENT

EMBARKING

EXCURSION

Flower Power

Fit the listed words into the grid below, then rearrange the letters in the shaded squares to form another word related to the theme of this book.

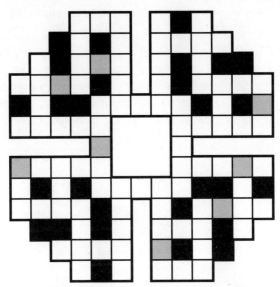

3 letters
BET
CAB
DAM
EGG
ELK
OPT
YET
ZOO

4 letters
AKIN
BIKE
BLOT
BOOM
BUNK
DENY

ETCH
HALO
LANE
RIND
SCUD
WAFT

5 letters
CHESS
ETHOS
GLASS
LIGHT
NORSE
OOZED

SABLE
TARDY
TATTY
TEASE
TYING
WAGON

**"A man is but the product
of his thoughts; what he
thinks, he becomes."**

Mahatma Gandhi

18   **Light Up**

Place circles (representing light bulbs) in some of the empty squares, in such a way that no two bulbs shine on each other, until every square of the grid is lit up. A bulb sends rays of light horizontally and vertically, illuminating its entire row and column unless its light is blocked by a black cell.

Some black cells contain numbers, indicating how many light bulbs are in adjacent squares either immediately above, below, to the right, or to the left. Bulbs placed diagonally adjacent to a numbered cell do not contribute to the bulb count. An unnumbered black cell may have any number of light bulbs adjacent to it, or none at all, and not all light bulbs are necessarily clued via black squares.

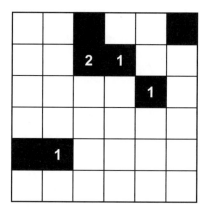

"Quiet the mind and the soul will speak."

Ma Jaya

Sudoku

Place one of the numbers from 1 to 9 into every empty cell so that each row, each column and each 3x3 block contains all the numbers from 1 to 9.

			5	2	9	6		
4	9	6		3		7		
			7		4	1		
5			3		1		6	
	3	8				4	2	
	6		4		2			1
		3	8		5			
		7		1		5	9	8
		5	9	7	6			

"Everything is based on mind,
is led by mind, is fashioned
by mind. If you speak
and act with a pure mind,
happiness will follow you, as
a shadow clings to a form."

Buddha

20   Maze

Start at the top and find a path to the middle of the maze.

 "No act of kindness, no matter how small, is ever wasted."

Aesop

21   Wordsearch: World Heritage Sites

Can you find all of the listed words hidden in the grid below?
Words run horizontally, vertically or diagonally, in either a forward or
backward direction.

```
A  N  J  A  R  O  E  T  E  M  O  I  I  O  X
D  N  T  I  M  G  E  D  B  L  A  Y  L  E  S
A  D  L  I  K  T  S  Z  D  R  U  D  A  G  D
S  Y  B  A  D  F  E  R  M  W  T  P  N  E  A
A  L  D  A  B  R  A  A  T  O  L  L  J  L  L
M  S  A  B  G  U  R  N  W  F  M  U  S  K  A
P  T  E  G  M  I  U  N  E  R  A  V  A  P  K
A  D  A  A  E  O  O  L  I  D  O  S  T  E  N
P  U  A  S  M  F  S  O  L  E  D  S  A  T  A
H  A  U  G  C  N  E  A  O  L  S  N  I  R  H
O  Q  Q  O  M  E  Y  R  M  C  E  L  H  A  C
S  O  R  I  Z  I  R  F  Y  M  N  G  T  U  T
Y  F  E  A  Y  I  T  W  U  T  F  R  Y  I  I
U  X  N  I  Y  A  N  B  C  H  A  V  I  N  A
O  F  A  L  I  X  A  T  A  J  M  A  H  A  L
```

ABU MENA	MASADA	ST KILDA
AKSUM	METEORA	TAJ MAHAL
ALDABRA ATOLL	MOUNT WUYI	TAXILA
ANJAR	OLD RAUMA	TIMGAD
CHAVIN	OLD TOWN OF CORFU	TIYA
DELOS	PAPHOS	TSODILO
HATRA	PETRA	TYRE
ITCHAN KALA	QUSEIR AMRA	YIN XU

Codeword

Every letter in this puzzle has been replaced by a number, the number remaining the same for that letter wherever it occurs. Every letter of the alphabet has been used. Substitute numbers for letters to complete the codeword.

It may help to cross off the letters beneath the grid to keep a track of progress, and to use the reference box showing which numbers have been decoded. Three letters have already been entered into the grid, to help you on your way.

6	4	25	23		13	9	13	9	23		5	3	4	16
3		6	3	9		23		10			10		23	
7	4	13	23		26	4	10	10	20	20		9		15
10		12		10		9			13	26	8	4	13	
	22	20	1	3		8	4	12	19			13		
2	19	9		3		24		8		9	16	16	20	14
23		6		13	19	23	15	21	26			14		20
17	14	4	18	21		8		24		23	18	4	6	20
20		23		20	12	14	20	18	18		17		6	
14	20	13	23	10		15		16		19		15	23	26
	26		9	7	20	8		16	26	10	20			
14	20	15	23	11		4		4		3			19	
23		23		26	23	2	8	20	6		16	23	21	20
4		13		26		16		23 A	8 N	16 T			23	
6	3	21	20		20	16	19	26	15		26	23	14	6

A B C D E F G H I J K L M

N O P Q R S T U V W X Y Z

1	2	3	4	5	6	7	8 N	9	10	11	12	13
14	15	16 T	17	18	19	20	21	22	23 A	24	25	26

Jigsaw

Which four shapes (two black and two white) can be fitted together to form the elephant shown here? The pieces may be rotated, but not flipped over.

24   Criss Cross: Cake Baking

The words are provided, but can you fit them all into the grid?

4 letters
BOWL
CAKE
EGGS
NUTS
TRAY

5 letters
AROMA
CREAM
FLOUR
FRUIT
ICING

MIXER
SPOON
SUGAR
WATER
YEAST

6 letters
BUTTER
GRATER
RECIPE
SPONGE

7 letters
BEATING
LOAF TIN
RAISINS
TESTING

8 letters
CHERRIES
CURRANTS
DECORATE

9 letters
PARCHMENT

25 Pyragram

Every clue in this puzzle is an anagram leading to a single-word solution. Correctly solve the anagram on each level of the pyramid and another word will appear, reading down the central column.

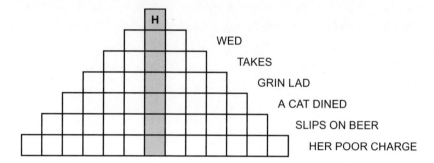

WED

TAKES

GRIN LAD

A CAT DINED

SLIPS ON BEER

HER POOR CHARGE

26 Word Ladder

Change one letter at a time (but not the position of any letter) to make a new word – and move from the word at the top of the ladder to the word at the bottom using the exact number of rungs provided.

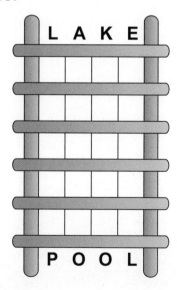

27   **Skyscrapers**

Place the numbers 1 to 5 into each row and column, one number per square. Each number represents a skyscraper of that many floors.

Arrange the skyscrapers in such a way that the given number outside the grid represents the number of buildings which can be seen from that point, looking only at that number's row or column.

A skyscraper with a lower number of floors cannot hide a higher building, but a one with a higher number of floors always hides any building behind it.

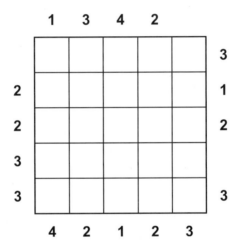

"Love starts when we push aside our ego and make room for someone else."

Rudolf Steiner

30

Wordsearch:
A Midsummer Night's Dream

Can you find all of the underlined words from this extract from William Shakespeare's "A Midsummer Night's Dream" hidden in the grid? Words run forward or backward, in either a horizontal, vertical, or diagonal direction.

```
N I D T E H T A L A B N O
E R E H T G L U I S O E T
N R I E A F L N N D W D E
I A P S E L A A D O P I E
B E O E D T K I N A R W W
D T N G I E N K R T N D S
O I A T H G P W L Y I A P
O U C S W O R H T U K N E
W Q R Y E E M Y H T S C E
E U E D S O M E T I M E L
N N V W W D X W T H G S S
M I O I O H E L I K E H S
K L G U R R E E I L N N N
B S T H G H D R W P D A A
E A R Y T H A V E Y S I B
```

I <u>know</u> a <u>bank</u> where the <u>wild</u> <u>thyme</u> <u>blows</u>,

Where <u>oxlips</u> and the <u>nodding</u> violet <u>grows</u>,

Quite <u>over-canopied</u> with luscious <u>woodbine</u>,

With <u>sweet</u> musk-roses and with <u>eglantine</u>:

There <u>sleeps</u> <u>Titania</u> <u>sometime</u> of the <u>night</u>,

<u>Lull'd</u> in <u>these</u> flowers with <u>dances</u> and delight;

And <u>there</u> the <u>snake</u> <u>throws</u> her enamell'd <u>skin</u>,

<u>Weed</u> <u>wide</u> <u>enough</u> to <u>wrap</u> a <u>fairy</u> in…

29 No Three in Line

Place either O or X into each empty square, so that no three consecutive squares in either a horizontal row or vertical column contain more than two of the same symbol.

There needs to be as many Os as Xs in every row and column.

O		X		X	O		X
O			O			X	
	X			O			
O			X	O	X		O
X	X		O			O	
O			O			X	
	X			O		O	O
	X	O		O			

"One of the most courageous decisions you'll ever make is to finally let go of what is hurting your heart and soul."

Brigitte Nicole

Sudoku

Place one of the numbers from 1 to 9 into every empty cell so that each row, each column and each 3x3 block contains all the numbers from 1 to 9.

		7			2	1	9	
3	1	2	9					
	4			6	5			7
		5		8			1	4
		3	6		4	5		
2	7			1		8		
8			7	4			3	
					1	7	8	5
	2	9	8			6		

"Who among us hasn't
envied a cat's ability to
ignore the cares of daily life
and to relax completely?"

Karen Brademeyer

Combiku

Each horizontal row and vertical column should contain four different shapes, and four different numbers.

Every square will contain one number and one shape, and no combination may be repeated anywhere else in the puzzle; so, for instance, if a square contains a 3 and a star, then no other square containing a 3 will also contain a star, and no other square with a star will also contain a 3.

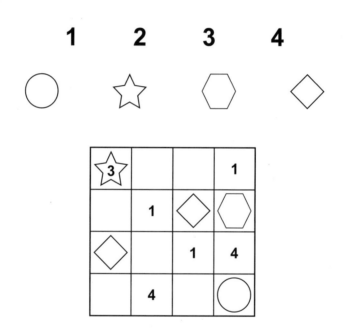

"Yesterday is gone. Tomorrow has not yet come. We have only today. Let us begin."

Mother Teresa

32   Shadow Play

Which of the shadows is that of the
pair of playful dolphins shown here?

33   Criss Cross: Flowers

The words are provided, but can you fit them all into the grid?

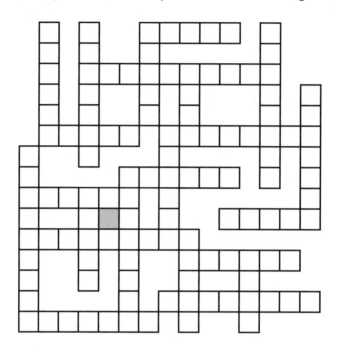

4 letters
IRIS
LILY

5 letters
DAISY
LILAC
LUPIN
STOCK
TANSY
TULIP

6 letters
CROCUS
DAHLIA
ORCHID
THRIFT
VIOLET

7 letters
ANEMONE
COWSLIP
GENTIAN

8 letters
BERGAMOT
CYCLAMEN
SCABIOUS
VALERIAN

9 letters
EDELWEISS
RUDBECKIA

10 letters
WALLFLOWER

34   Wordsearch: In the Greenhouse

Can you find all of the listed words hidden in the grid below?
Words run horizontally, vertically or diagonally, in either a forward or
backward direction.

```
A R G H A R O T A G A P O R P
S F K E T S R N E S L Y I V C
D E R U R I C A W P F D E T V
E T X A L M H R F I D A V O E
E L A O N O I T A L U S N I G
S F R M B C D N E C I H S L E
E L E L P U H A A R B E T H T
H O C T G E S M E T S L O Y A
C W A S S T R B I T I F E G B
O E S T C O M P O S T O L E L
L R A E F U E P E R E A N H E
C K S S C A R T O W S C N L S
E N B U O M S W M S H O U G T
I F C A S I E V E E I M A E S
U W A T E L L M S A U T E R F
```

BENCHES	GLASS	SHELF
BOXES	INSECTS	SIEVE
CLIPS	INSULATION	SOIL
CLOCHE	ORCHID	STAKE
COMPOST	POTS	TAGS
CUCUMBER	PROPAGATOR	TAMPER
FLOWER	RIDDLE	TROWEL
GERMINATION	SEEDS	VEGETABLES

Maze

Start at the top and find a path to the middle of the maze.

"The purpose of meditation
practice is not enlightenment;
it is to pay attention even at
unextraordinary times, to be of the
present, nothing-but-the-present,
to bear this mindfulness of now
into each event of ordinary life."

Peter Matthiessen

Logi-5

Every row and column of this grid should contain one each of the letters A, B, C, D, and E.

In addition, each of the five shapes (marked by thicker lines) should also contain one each of the letters A, B, C, D, and E.

Can you complete the grid?

		C	E	
	C	D		E
			C	
E		A		
	D			

"Growth is painful. Change is painful. But nothing is as painful as staying stuck somewhere you don't belong."

Mandy Hale

37   Wordsearch: Warm Words

Can you find all of the listed words hidden in the grid below?
Words run horizontally, vertically or diagonally, in either a forward or
backward direction.

```
T Y T I C I R T C E L E F P E
K A L Y N B S E G U V E E A H
E Z I C K S Z U K L T Y V S E
R E U W O U U E N A O D E S A
O T Q Y R M W L R N S W R I T
S R U P R A F E A F Y E I O I
E O I M R A P O I T U J S N N
N P L M Z M D P R E E Z H F G
E I S I E B F I E T S A M I O
Y C U T U S L V A D E I Y R F
J A M G E N I A L T U R R E C
B L M I R U A S N E O P T S O
E B E A D G D O A K Z R L I V
L S R V B F L U S H E D U D E
M E Y E V A W T A E H T S E R
```

BLANKET   GLOWING   RADIATOR

COMFORTER   HEAT WAVE   SNUG

COVER   HEATING   SULTRY

ELECTRICITY   INSULATE   SUMMERY

FEVERISH   KEROSENE   SUNNY

FIRESIDE   LUKEWARM   TEMPERATE

FLUSHED   PASSION   TROPICAL

GENIAL   QUILT   WRAPPED UP

Sudoku

Place one of the numbers from 1 to 9 into every empty cell so that each row, each column and each 3x3 block contains all the numbers from 1 to 9.

	9	5			7	3		
		6	8		3		4	
				4	6	2	7	
3				2	4			5
1		9				4		2
2			9	3				6
	4	2	3	5				
	7		1		9	8		
		8	4			9	5	

"When I let go of what I am, I become what I might be."

Lao Tzu,

39 Codeword

Every letter in this puzzle has been replaced by a number, the number remaining the same for that letter wherever it occurs. Every letter of the alphabet has been used. Substitute numbers for letters to complete the codeword.

It may help to cross off the letters beneath the grid to keep a track of progress, and to use the reference box showing which numbers have been decoded. Three letters have already been entered into the grid, to help you on your way.

13	22	3	15	11	23		6	11	2	23	20	11	10	14
14		9		18			8		1		5			22
2	23	23	22	19	11	23		8		5	11	7	1	18
12		22		22		2	18	11	18	22		22		18
16	15	26	20	23	22	7		2		23	11	18	10	22
11			2		10	1	11	5	13	22		10		23
10	23	2	18	10	24		7 **D**		6	2	7	9		
14			19		1	3	2 **I**	7	22		2			20
		16	1	14	22		22 **E**		5	11	21	11	19	22
25		11		11	7	7	15	10	22		11			8
15	12	13	22	6		11		9	1	15	18	19	22	5
11		26		9	11	4	18	13		13		5		2
2	21	2	22	7		7		6	5	11	12	22	17	22
18		18		2		23			19		22			18
6	5	22	18	7	2	22	5		21	22	18	6	22	7

A B C D E F G H I J K L M
N O P Q R S T U V W X Y Z

1	2 **I**	3	4	5	6	7 **D**	8	9	10	11	12	13
14	15	16	17	18	19	20	21	22 **E**	23	24	25	26

42

40   Wordsearch: Birthday Party

Can you find all of the listed words hidden in the grid below?
Words run horizontally, vertically or diagonally, in either a forward or
backward direction.

```
S W E R Y A N S T E R A L B E
E I S K D L E C E U Y E A P M
L S M U N T I S W P M S X P E
D R K A A O P M P X S T M A H
N E J L E E I A A E R F A P T
A N P B E R H T S F R I R E E
C N Y C R U C S A I O G Q R S
U A H A E L A E E T L B U H I
A B E C O L C N C C I D E A R
C E R W G J D W E I A V E T P
E I N W I S H E S S A R N S R
I D S E M A G U E S T S D I U
P L A U G H T E R B K K P S S
E K E M M B E B A L L O O N S
Y U S E K A C R I N A S E L E
```

BALLOONS	GAMES	MARQUEE
BANNERS	GIFTS	MUSIC
CAKES	GLASSES	PAPER HATS
CANDLES	GUESTS	PLATES
CARDS	HAPPY	SPEECH
CLOWN	ICE CREAM	SURPRISE
FAMILY	INVITATION	THEME
FRIENDS	LAUGHTER	WISHES

41   Coin Collecting

In this puzzle, an amateur coin collector has been out with his metal detector, searching for booty. He didn't have time to dig up all the coins he found, so has made a grid map, showing their locations, in the hope that if he loses the map, at least no-one else will understand it... However, he didn't count on YOU coming across the strange grid (as seen here). Will you be able to discover the correct number of coins and their precise locations?

Those squares containing numbers are empty, but where a number appears in a square, it indicates how many coins are located in the squares (up to a maximum of eight) surrounding the numbered one, touching it at any corner or side. There is only one coin in any individual square.

Place a circle into every square containing a coin.

1	1	2		2	1		1
2				4		4	
2			2				2
	3	2			5	5	
	2		1	1			
2					2	5	
	2			1	2	3	
2							2

"Doing the best at this moment puts you in the best place for the next moment."

Oprah Winfrey

Flower Power

Fit the listed words into the grid below, then rearrange the letters in the shaded squares to form another word related to the theme of this book.

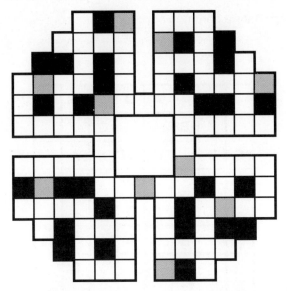

3 letters	4 letters		5 letters	
ACT	BEAK	LOAF	ARGON	INCUR
ADO	BIAS	ONUS	AVERT	LASSO
BUS	BOSS	PUMP	BLAZE	MANGO
BUT	BYTE	SHOP	COWER	RATIO
CRY	EMIR	STEW	CRUEL	SMELT
ROE	LINK	YOGA	FLUTE	TUTOR
TUG				
WIN				

**"Every thought we think
is creating our future."**

Louise Hay

43   Patchwork

Every square should be filled with a letter from A to D, and each heavily outlined set of four squares should contain four different letters. Every row and column must contain two of each letter.

Squares that share a common border may not contain the same letter.

		A	C		D	C	
	B			C			
C	D		B			A	
D	B			B			
		C		D	C		
				A			
		A				C	
C	B		A		B		A

"When we meditate we expand, spreading our wings like a bird, trying to enter consciously into Infinity, Eternity and Immortality, welcoming them into our aspiring consciousness."

Sri Chinmoy

44　Slitherlink

Draw a single continuous loop, by connecting the dots. No line may cross the path of another.

The figure inside each set of any four surrounding dots indicates the total number of surrounding lines.

```
.  .  .  .  .     .  .  .  .
  2  2  2  2  2     1  2  2
.  .  .  .  .  .  .  .  .  .
  2     2  3  2  3  3  3  2
.  .  .  .  .  .  .  .  .  .
           2     1  1  1
.  .  .  .  .  .  .  .  .  .
     2  2  1  2  0  1  2  2
.  .  .  .  .  .  .  .  .  .
  1           3  3     2
.  .  .  .  .  .  .  .  .  .
     2     1     2  1
.  .  .  .  .  .  .  .  .  .
  2  2  3  3              2
.  .  .  .  .  .  .  .  .  .
     2  1     1  2  2  2
.  .  .  .  .  .  .  .  .  .
  3     3  3  3  2  3  2
.  .  .  .  .  .  .  .  .  .
```

"Let come what comes, let go what goes. See what remains."

Ramana Maharshi

Sudoku

Place one of the numbers from 1 to 9 into every empty cell so that each row, each column and each 3x3 block contains all the numbers from 1 to 9.

				5	2	3		9
5	1					2	7	
6				9		8	4	
	2		7			6		
3	8		4		1		9	7
		5			9		8	
	9	8		4				3
	6	3					5	1
7		4	2	1				

"Life is ten percent
what happens to you
and ninety percent how
you respond to it."

Charles Swindoll

46   **Wordsearch: Swimming Pool**

Can you find all of the listed words hidden in the grid below?
Words run horizontally, vertically or diagonally, in either a forward or
backward direction.

```
T  A  M  F  T  N  A  D  N  E  T  T  A  P  E
R  W  S  E  Y  M  J  A  W  U  A  R  S  F  R
E  H  S  A  L  P  S  B  K  K  E  I  O  A  M
T  I  E  D  R  A  U  G  E  F  I  L  L  D  S
A  S  L  E  Y  L  A  A  R  W  D  R  A  I  N
W  T  C  L  A  D  D  E  R  N  W  A  R  B  O
F  L  S  E  Y  I  S  G  X  S  H  O  W  E  R
T  E  U  A  P  H  N  E  E  E  S  I  A  P  K
R  L  M  P  M  I  I  D  M  C  R  A  W  L  E
U  A  G  E  T  C  I  S  M  U  A  C  Z  E  L
N  E  N  A  E  L  G  R  C  I  T  F  I  V  R
K  T  O  B  S  S  L  E  W  O  T  S  K  S  A
S  L  S  E  H  G  W  S  Y  S  T  R  O  K  E
F  L  U  M  E  P  B  O  Y  T  R  A  P  C  J
M  A  T  T  E  O  S  P  V  E  R  A  N  E  G
```

ATTENDANT	LADDER	SNORKEL
BRAWN	LIFEGUARD	SPLASH
COSTUME	MUSCLE	STROKE
CRAWL	PARTY	TAKE A DIP
DRAIN	POSERS	TOWELS
EXERCISE	REFRESH- MENTS	TRUNKS
FLOATING		WATER
FLUME	SHOWER	WHISTLE
	SLIDES	

Every letter in this puzzle has been replaced by a number, the number remaining the same for that letter wherever it occurs. Every letter of the alphabet has been used. Substitute numbers for letters to complete the codeword.

It may help to cross off the letters beneath the grid to keep a track of progress, and to use the reference box showing which numbers have been decoded. Three letters have already been entered into the grid, to help you on your way.

18	12	1	21	20	2	■	11	8	9	18	21	1	9	9
12	■	3	■	6	■	14	■	18	■	12	■	26	■	25
1	17	1	20	18	■	24	25	18	23	24	26	6	21	16
1	■	16	■	6	21	13	■	6	■	3	■	9	■	8
18	1	8	■	4	■	1	9	20	8	3	8	18	24	12
24	■	21	■	1	■	■	1	■	5	■	15	■	21	■
5	8	18	1	21	18	1	7	■	12	8	19	19	6	18
■	7	■	21	■	1	■	25	■	24	■	1	■	24	■
10	24	24	7	1	21	■	20	24	21	23	12	24	21	18
■	12	■	24	■	1	■	1	■	■	24	■	11	■	12
9	21	24	10	9	18	24	12	15	■	25	■	1	14	1
22	■	8	■	20	■	23	■	24	10	21	■	12	■	8
25	21	13	21	24 N	18 O	18 T	1	7	■	7	12	1	8	7
6	■	1	■	10	■	1	■	1	■	1	■	8	■	3
19	25	21	16	3	6	21	16	■	10	12	6	18	2	1

A B C D E F G H I J K L M

N O P Q R S T U V W X Y Z

1	2	3	4	5	6	7	8	9	10	11	12	13
14	15	16	17	18 **T**	19	20	21 **N**	22	23	24 **O**	25	26

48   Sudoku

Place one of the numbers from 1 to 9 into every empty cell so that each row, each column and each 3x3 block contains all the numbers from 1 to 9.

			6	3	2			
	1	8		7			4	3
	6					7		5
		1	7			4	5	2
6			3		4			7
4	7	9			1	8		
7		5					1	
3	8			1		2	6	
			4	9	3			

"If you wait for tomorrow,
tomorrow comes. If you
don't wait for tomorrow,
tomorrow comes."

Senegalese proverb

Criss Cross: Time for Bed

The words are provided, but can you fit them all into the grid?

3 letters
BED
COT

4 letters
BATH
LAMP
REST
SNUG
YAWN

5 letters
COCOA
RELAX

6 letters
DOZING
PILLOW
SHEETS
SLEEPY
SNOOZE
WARMTH

7 letters
COMFORT
LULLABY
PRAYERS
SNORING
WASHING

8 letters
MATTRESS

9 letters
NIGHTGOWN
UNDRESSED

10 letters
ALARM CLOCK

50   Calcudoku

Each row and column should contain different numbers from 1 to 6.

The numbers placed in a heavily outlined set of squares may be repeated, but must produce the calculation in the top left corner, using the mathematical symbol provided: multiply (x), divide (/), add (+), and subtract (–).

For example, when multiplied, the numbers 4 and 3 total 12:

12x	
4	**3**

4/		1–		11+	
2/		15x	3/	5+	
60x				8x	2/
	6/		100x		
2/	8+				2/
	9+		3/		

 "Change your life today. Don't gamble on the future, act now, without delay."

Simone de Beauvoir

Bridges

Join the circular islands by drawing horizontal or vertical lines to represent bridges, in such a way that the number of bridges connected to each island must match the number on that island. No bridge may cross another, and no more than two bridges can join any pair of islands.

The finished design will allow you to travel from one island to any other island on the map.

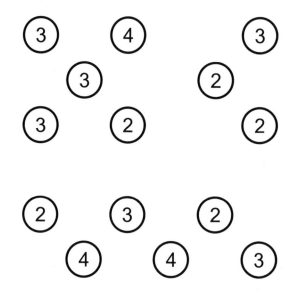

"Each moment is a chance
for us to make peace
with the world, to make
peace possible for the
world, to make happiness
possible for the world."

Thich Nhat Hanh

Wordsearch: Movies

Can you find all of the listed words hidden in the grid below?
Words run horizontally, vertically or diagonally, in either a forward or
backward direction.

```
S P U D N C A I D O Z S E R A
R T R Y R O T S Y O T L N A S
E T B E N E O U L R Y R O P T
T Z O D I A S T L P N I I N E
S S I L E N C E A A U G T U R
I J E Z E B E L F L H L I G A
S U E D A M A H Y E P A N P I
N O R B I T A S K R F I O O N
L T E T B S S C S I E R M T M
F E F V H E T H L D D E E O A
T R R T S A A U N E V T R O N
E A O N A M R O R R B A P T L
R B S Z P C R V F B C M E S I
O A H O E A E R E N I E W I D
S C O I L N A N D Y R A G E E
```

AMADEUS

CABARET

CAMELOT

DISTURBIA

FROZEN

HARVEY

JEZEBEL

LA RONDE

MATERIAL
GIRLS

NORBIT

PALE RIDER

PLATOON

PREMONITION

RAIN MAN

SHAMPOO

SILENCE

SISTERS

SKYFALL

TOOTSIE

TOP GUN

TOY STORY

ULYSSES

WEINER

ZODIAC

53   Criss Cross: Types of Literature

The words are provided, but can you fit them all into the grid?

4 letters
EPIC
PULP
SAGA

5 letters
CRIME
ESSAY
NOVEL
ROMAN
TRIAD
VERSE

6 letters
COMEDY
PARODY
SATIRE
THESIS

7 letters
EPISTLE
FANTASY
FICTION
POLEMIC
TRAGEDY

8 letters
ALLEGORY
APOLOGUE
LIBRETTO

9 letters
BIOGRAPHY
CHILDREN'S

Sudoku

Place one of the numbers from 1 to 9 into every empty cell so that each row, each column and each 3x3 block contains all the numbers from 1 to 9.

9			1		2			3
	2	4		9	7			5
		7				1		2
	1	6	2	8				
	9		6		3		4	
				7	4	5	6	
8		1				3		
6			8	5		7	2	
5			4		6			9

"Silence fertilizes the
deep place where
personality grows. A life
with a peaceful centre can
weather all storms."

Norman Vincent Peale

55   Codeword

Every letter in this puzzle has been replaced by a number, the number remaining the same for that letter wherever it occurs. Every letter of the alphabet has been used. Substitute numbers for letters to complete the codeword.

It may help to cross off the letters beneath the grid to keep a track of progress, and to use the reference box showing which numbers have been decoded. Three letters have already been entered into the grid, to help you on your way.

13	15	14	14	19	22	3	5	■	17	22	19	17	6	14 **E**
■	11	■	18	■	23	■	23	1	14	■	14	■	■	3 **N**
14	25	12	11	2	11	17	14	■	11	20	11	13	14	26 **D**
■	1	■	17	■	17	■	11	■	6	■	12	■		
20	■	23	14	9	14	12	17	6	23	1	■	11	23	10
23	■	14	■	11	■	23	■	2	■	9	■	23	■	11
6	20	21	14	12	17	22	2	14	■	23	14	22	5	3
15	■	6	■	14	■	10	■	23	■	22	■	9	■	11
13	24	22	10	19	■	13	7	16	14	14	8	22	3	5
14	■	3	■	11	■	6	■	13	■	3	■	14	■	14
23	6	26	■	12	6	3	17	14	3	26	14	23	■	23
■	■	14	■	24	■	■	11	■	11	■	23	■	5	■
4	11	23	11	13	13	■	19	11	13	13	11	20	18	14
6	■	■	18	■	11	5	14	■	11	■	13	■	14	■
19	11	18	18	22	26	■	23	14	18	22	14	2	14	26

A B C D E F G H I J K L M

N O P Q R S T U V W X Y Z

1	2	3 **N**	4	5	6	7	8	9	10	11	12	13
14 **E**	15	16	17	18	19	20	21	22	23	24	25	26 **D**

56   Jigsaw

Which four shapes (two black and
two white) can be fitted together to
form the cat shown here? The pieces
may be rotated, but not flipped over.

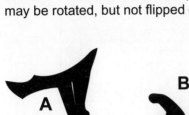

A

B

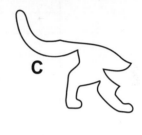

C

D

E

F

G

H

I

J

K

L

M

57   Criss Cross: Varieties of Apple

The words are provided, but can you fit them all into the grid?

4 letters
COX'S
ENVY
JAZZ
KATY

5 letters
AKANE
MUTSU
SONYA

6 letters
FIESTA
HAWAII
IDARED

7 letters
ALKMENE
CARROLL
MALINDA
WAGENER
WEALTHY

8 letters
CATSHEAD

9 letters
DISCOVERY
EDWARD VII
ST CECILIA

10 letters
HONEYCRISP

11 letters
CHARLES ROSS

Wordsearch: Shades of Pink

Can you find all of the listed words hidden in the grid below?
Words run horizontally, vertically or diagonally, in either a forward or backward direction.

```
H M O S S O L B Y R R E H C A
T Y J F A N D A N G O O I B P
N R E V O L G X O F E E T E R
A R A W R E D N E V A L M E I
R E W C H I N A P I N K S I C
A B S C H E D D A R P I N K O
M W K O A N M A C C R O A S T
A A G P L R A V I E N N I A A
P R U N O F N I C N P E S I M
P T E L I W E A L M P A H S A
E S R N T K D R T U E R C A R
A P A T U R C E I I H G U L I
C E R I S V A O R N O T F M S
H A T N E G A M H D O N N O K
N A I S R E P R O S E P I N K
```

AMARANTH	FOXGLOVE	ROSE PINK
APRICOT	FUCHSIA	SALMON
CARNATION	LAVENDER	SHOCKING
CERISE	MAGENTA	SOLFERINO
CHEDDAR PINK	PEACH	STRAWBERRY
CHERRY BLOSSOM	PEONY	TAMARISK
CHINA PINK	PERSIAN	THULIAN
FANDANGO	POWDER	ULTRA

59   No Four in Line

Place either O or X into each empty square, so that no four consecutive squares in a straight line in any direction (horizontally, vertically, or diagonally) contain more than three of the same symbol.

O	X		O		O	O	O	
	O	O	O			O	O	
X		O		O			O	X
	X			O		X		
		O	O			X		
X		O		O			O	
		X				O		X
O		X	X	X		O	X	X
X	O	X				X	X	X

"Training your mind to be
in the present moment
is the #1 key to making
healthier choices."

Susan Albers

60   Pyragram

Every clue in this puzzle is an anagram leading to a single-word solution. Correctly solve the anagram on each level of the pyramid and another word will appear, reading down the central column.

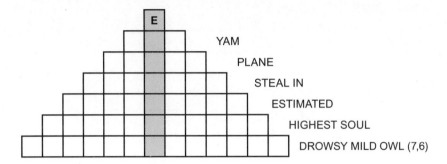

YAM

PLANE

STEAL IN

ESTIMATED

HIGHEST SOUL

DROWSY MILD OWL (7,6)

61   Word Wheel

How many words of three or more letters can you make from those in the wheel, without using plurals, abbreviations or proper nouns?

The central letter must appear once in every word and no letter in a section of the wheel may be used more than once.

There is at least one nine-letter word in the wheel.

Nine-letter word(s):

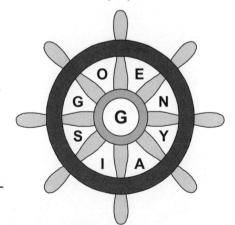

_____

Futoshiki

Fill the grid so that every horizontal row and vertical column contains all the numbers 1 to 6.

Any arrows in the grid always point toward a square that contains a lower number.

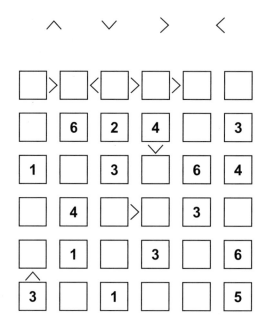

"If you come from a place of love then you are free and fear dispels itself into nothing. If you live in the moment – in the present – then you don't fear because you can let all the good, the miracles, in."

Cat Forsley

Sudoku

Place one of the numbers from 1 to 9 into every empty cell so that each row, each column and each 3x3 block contains all the numbers from 1 to 9.

					7		5	6
5		2		9	3		8	
	6	7			2	3		
		5			4		6	1
8			2		6			7
1	4		8			9		
		1	3			4	2	
	2		7	5		1		3
9	8		4					

"No valid plans for the future can be made by those who have no capacity for living now."

Alan Watts

64   Domino Placement

A standard set of 28 dominoes has been laid out as shown. Can you draw in the edges of them all?

The check-box is provided as an aid, so that you can see which dominoes have been located.

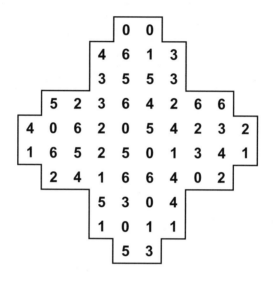

0-0	0-1	0-2	0-3	0-4	0-5	0-6	1-1	1-2	1-3	1-4	1-5	1-6	2-2

2-3	2-4	2-5	2-6	3-3	3-4	3-5	3-6	4-4	4-5	4-6	5-5	5-6	6-6

"No age is too early
or too late for the
health of the soul."

Epicurus

Wordsearch: Marine Life

Can you find all of the listed words hidden in the grid below?
Words run horizontally, vertically or diagonally, in either a forward or backward direction.

```
E M E S C E K C O D D I P M E
S A B A R U L E B D K D T B S
R N E E U K D H C N O C A H U
O A I A S K N A R P L R S N R
H T R I T O N U O A N I R M K
A E H A A T H R H A F E I R A
E E E B C L T W C E T E A O R
S S L R E S R L L S B H O W A
W H G S A A E T B A S N T P S
I R S G N I T O E K V E M I P
A U A E T U L O V B P E U H M
M Z N C C O R A L M A D R S I
L L I R K A S T I O N T E C R
L O R R A B A L O N E T X P H
A F F O L L E H S K S U T E S
```

ABALONE	LAVER	SEAHORSE
BARNACLE	LIMPET	SHARK
CONCH	LOBSTER	SHIPWORM
CORAL	MANATEE	SHRIMP
CRUSTACEAN	MUREX	TRITON
CUTTLEFISH	MUSSEL	TUSK SHELL
GASTROPOD	NARWHAL	VOLUTE
KRILL	PIDDOCK	WRACK

66   Criss Cross: Herbs and Spices

The words are provided, but can you fit them all into the grid?

4 letters
MACE
SAGE

5 letters
ANISE
CAPER
CUMIN
SENNA
THYME

6 letters
CASSIA
FENNEL
GARLIC
HYSSOP
LOVAGE
SORREL

7 letters
CATMINT
CAYENNE
CHERVIL
MUSTARD

8 letters
MARJORAM

9 letters
CORIANDER
HYPERICUM
LEMON BALM

11 letters
HORSERADISH
ST JOHN'S
WORT

67 Flower Power

Fit the listed words into the grid below, then rearrange the letters in the shaded squares to form another word related to the theme of this book.

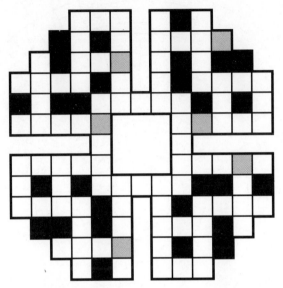

3 letters

AIM
AWL
JAB
JUT
NOW
NUN
OIL
PRY

4 letters

AFAR   PACK
BOLD   PLAY
DAME   SNUG
DEFT   TAXI
JUNE   TICK
JURY   YAWN

5 letters

ASKEW   SALTY
GHOST   SCOOP
GLOWS   SWISS
JEANS   TOWEL
MIRTH   TRUSS
RETRY   WOMAN

"The brain is wider than the sky."

Emily Dickinson

68 **Maze**

Start at the top and find a path to the middle of the maze.

"When you follow your bliss
... doors will open where
you would not have thought
there would be doors; and
where there wouldn't be a
door for anyone else."

Joseph Campbell

In Place

Place the listed words horizontally into the grid, so that when read from top left to bottom right, the letters in the shaded squares spell out a word linked to the theme of this book. Some letters are already in place.

ADMIRAL

CRUMBLE

GALLERY

HAMMOCK

PERFECT

SCARLET

WORKBOX

"Don't worry about what the world needs. Ask what makes you come alive and do that. Because what the world needs is people who have come alive."

Howard Thurman

70   Jigsaw

Which four shapes (two black and two white) can be
fitted together to form the Buddha can shown here?
The pieces may be rotated, but not flipped over.

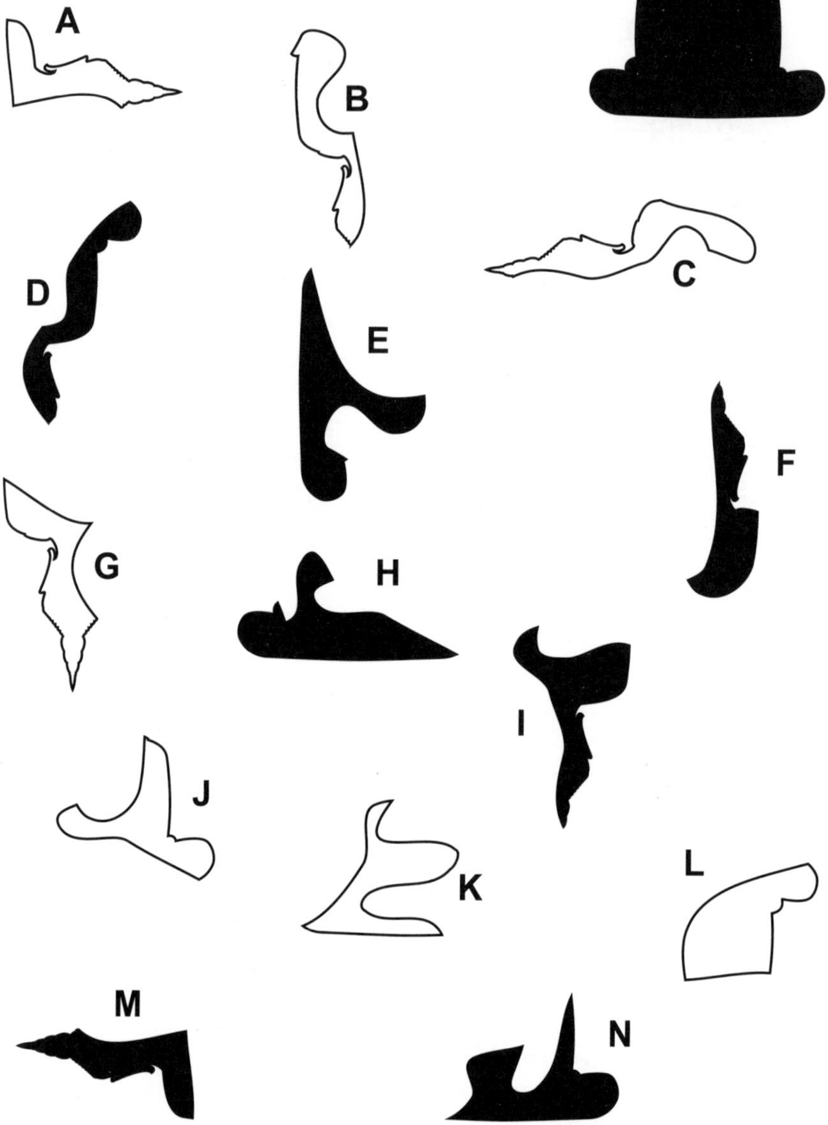

A

B

C

D

E

F

G

H

I

J

K

L

M

N

71 Wordsearch: Rivers of Africa

Can you find all of the listed words hidden in the grid below?
Words run horizontally, vertically or diagonally, in either a forward or
backward direction.

```
U  J  U  R  I  G  N  A  B  U  E  S  E  Y  A
G  E  U  E  P  A  U  O  N  I  L  A  H  Y  A
T  R  U  B  H  E  A  C  A  V  A  L  L  A  W
I  U  A  T  B  A  R  A  H  K  W  A  N  G  O
M  C  R  E  G  A  U  O  Z  I  M  T  L  L  M
A  U  U  B  A  N  E  I  T  D  G  L  R  U  E
M  A  V  O  E  Z  S  E  V  U  P  O  P  A  R
O  N  U  U  F  V  N  O  L  A  P  V  R  P  E
L  D  M  R  Z  I  I  A  O  U  R  A  P  T  G
K  O  A  E  E  A  G  L  U  T  C  E  M  N  I
C  U  D  G  L  E  M  W  L  C  M  Z  G  I  N
O  B  N  R  N  A  L  B  M  E  L  A  A  A  S
N  E  A  E  E  L  I  N  E  U  L  B  G  S  K
G  H  S  G  N  C  A  T  E  Z  I  M  B  A  A
O  T  E  G  H  E  L  L  I  U  I  R  Y  E  S
```

ATBARAH	JUBBA	OTEGHELLI
BLUE NILE	KAGERA	RUVUMA
BOU REGREG	KUNENE	SAINT PAUL
CAVALLA	KWANGO	SENEGAL
CONGO	LOMAMI	TURBEVILLE
CUANDO	MAPUTO	UBANGI
CUANZA	NIGER	VOLTA
GAMTOOS	ONILAHY	ZAMBEZI

72   Codeword

Every letter in this puzzle has been replaced by a number, the number remaining the same for that letter wherever it occurs. Every letter of the alphabet has been used. Substitute numbers for letters to complete the codeword.

It may help to cross off the letters beneath the grid to keep a track of progress, and to use the reference box showing which numbers have been decoded. Three letters have already been entered into the grid, to help you on your way.

13	26	20	18	25	5	■	21	■	20	■	24	1	20	16
26	■	1	■	14	■	1	9	23	1	26	7	■	■	20
7	25	15	14	9	3	7	8	■	5	■	24	14	21	9
13	■	14	■	10	■	19		18	21	23	24	■	■	18
13	21	26	16	14	2	1	1	15	■	26	21	12	25	
■	10	■	■	1	■	■	1	5	9	14	■	5		
9	21	23	16	2	21	3	17	26	14	■	5	21	8	14
■	18	■	14	■	22	■	18	■	25	■	7	■	7	■
6	26	7	23	■	14	23	6	26	1	20	23	14	25	8
18	■	■	21	12	9	20	■	23	■	■	18			
4	7	18	6	■	8	1	26	14	9	21	25	3	14	
7	■	2	7	16	2	■	18	■	7	■	1	■	25	
21	26	8	1	■	18	■	11	21 (A)	18 (I)	26 (L)	24	18	9	15
25	■	9	21	8	2	14	9	■	14	■	16		14	
8	21	17	14	■	14	■	8	■	13	9	18	14	25	15

A B C D E F G H I J K L M
N O P Q R S T U V W X Y Z

1	2	3	4	5	6	7	8	9	10	11	12	13
14	15	16	17	18 (I)	19	20	21 (A)	22	23	24	25	26 (L)

Sudoku

Place one of the numbers from 1 to 9 into every empty cell so that each row, each column and each 3x3 block contains all the numbers from 1 to 9.

2			7		3			
5			4	6	8			
7				9		8	3	5
		5	9		2		4	
3		6				9		1
	2		3		6	5		
4	1	8		2				7
			8	7	5			4
			1		4			9

"Tension is who you think
you should be. Relaxation
is who you are."

Chinese proverb

Criss Cross: Wedding Day

The words are provided, but can you fit them all into the grid?

4 letters
CARS
VOWS
WIFE

5 letters
AISLE
ALTAR
BRIDE
DRESS
PAGES
RINGS
ROSES

TIARA
TRAIN
VICAR

6 letters
CAMERA
GARTER
SMILES

7 letters
BEST MAN
HUSBAND
SERVICE

8 letters
CEREMONY
CONFETTI
FREESIAS

9 letters
BETROTHED
CELEBRATE
TELEGRAMS

10 letters
BUTTONHOLE

75   Pyragram

Every clue in this puzzle is an anagram leading to a single-word solution. Correctly solve the anagram on each level of the pyramid and another word will appear, reading down the central column.

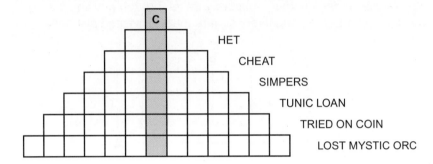

HET

CHEAT

SIMPERS

TUNIC LOAN

TRIED ON COIN

LOST MYSTIC ORC

76   Word Ladder

Change one letter at a time (but not the position of any letter) to make a new word – and move from the word at the top of the ladder to the word at the bottom using the exact number of rungs provided.

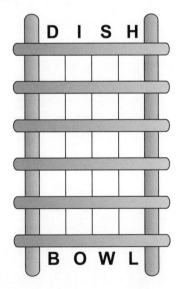

Number Link

Working from one square to another, horizontally or vertically (never diagonally), draw single continuous paths to pair up each set of two matching numbers.

No line may cross another, none may travel through any square containing a number, and every square must be visited just once.

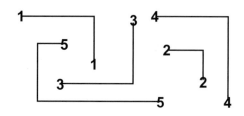

8						6	10	2
	7	4						
	1		1					
	11				7			
		3						
		5			6	2	10	
			11		4			
		5	3					12
8				12	9			9

"Awareness in itself is healing."

Frederick Salomon Perls

Wordsearch:
Moonlight, Summer Moonlight

Can you find all of the underlined words from the poem "Moonlight,
Summer Moonlight" by Emily Brontë hidden in the grid? Words run
forward or backward, in either a horizontal, vertical, or diagonal
direction.

```
M O R F E W F R L R Z D S
G O E T I A U O T E H N E
A E F E A V V G R M N U E
R O N G R E T I U M T O S
S L M T L E A S E U E R D
T Y E Y L F H L O S E E A
Y S E N L Y O T E M W M E
D K S C D S B H O S S E H
L O S H H I T O T R E E S
I I L G E A N E W H E S R
W H U A E L E G D E A A E
I O I R I P T A R R R S W
B E B G E D E E G E O S O
L V H D H O U R R H E S L
S T A P T L L I T S D N F
```

'Tis <u>moonlight</u>, <u>summer</u> moonlight,
All <u>soft</u> and <u>still</u> and <u>fair</u>;
The <u>solemn</u> <u>hour</u> of midnight
<u>Breathes</u> <u>sweet</u> thoughts everywhere,

But <u>most</u> where <u>trees</u> are sending
Their breezy <u>boughs</u> on <u>high</u>,
Or stooping low are <u>lending</u>
A <u>shelter</u> <u>from</u> the <u>sky</u>.

And <u>there</u> in <u>those</u> <u>wild</u> <u>bowers</u>
A <u>lovely</u> <u>form</u> is <u>laid</u>;
<u>Green</u> <u>grass</u> and <u>dew-steeped</u> <u>flowers</u>
<u>Wave</u> <u>gently</u> <u>round</u> her <u>head</u>.

Logi-6

Every row and column of this grid should contain one each of the letters A, B, C, D, E, and F.

In addition, each of the six shapes (marked by thicker lines) should also contain one each of the letters A, B, C, D, E, and F.

Can you complete the grid?

				D	E
	F				C
		E	A		
				F	
	E	C	D	A	

"You must learn to let go.
Release the stress.
You were never in
control anyway."

Steve Maraboli

Sudoku

Place one of the numbers from 1 to 9 into every empty cell so that each row, each column and each 3x3 block contains all the numbers from 1 to 9.

4	6			9	7		2	
		8		3			1	6
9	3	5	1					
			4	2		7		
5		2				1		4
		7		5	8			
					6	3	7	9
3	2			8		4		
	1		9	4			8	5

"We shape clay into a pot, but it is the emptiness inside that holds whatever we want."

Lao Tzu

Codeword

Every letter in this puzzle has been replaced by a number, the number remaining the same for that letter wherever it occurs. Every letter of the alphabet has been used. Substitute numbers for letters to complete the codeword.

It may help to cross off the letters beneath the grid to keep a track of progress, and to use the reference box showing which numbers have been decoded. Three letters have already been entered into the grid, to help you on your way.

12	9	7	12	10	16	10	14	9		9		17		11
18		23		6		9		11	4	4	20	9	12	
11	26	13	24	16	11	7	16	12		10		11		4
19			16		7		17	11	16	11	6	6	18	
9	21	17	18	9	2	24	9	6		23		10 I		5
7			9		24		9	20	8		23 O		21	
	15	23	6	17	10	25	20	9		9	7	7 N	24	10
9			20		20		5		12		23		11	
4	23	20	5	4		4	9	26	11	7	16	10	17	
10		23		9	6	11		6		23		23		
20		22		6		1	10	7	26	4	6	23	23	15
9	21	9	17	24	16	9			23		10		15	
4		7		12		6	11	10	7	17	23	11	16	12
12	10	3	7	11	20		10		10		24		9	
5		9		20		25	20	11	17	19	12	4	23	16

A B C D E F G H I J K L M

N O P Q R S T U V W X Y Z

1	2	3	4	5	6	7 N	8	9	10 I	11	12	13
14	15	16	17	18	19	20	21	22	23 O	24	25	26

Reflections

Which of the designs below is an exact horizontal (left to right) mirror image of the design to the right?

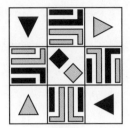

I

2

3

4

5

6

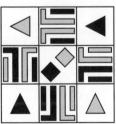

7

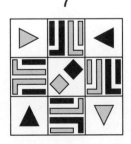

8

83   Criss Cross: Wood Types

The words are provided, but can you fit them all into the grid?

3 letters
ASH
ELM
FIR
OAK
YEW

4 letters
DEAL
PINE
TEAK

5 letters
ALDER
BALSA
BEECH
BRIAR
HAZEL
LARCH
MAPLE
OLIVE

6 letters
POPLAR
WICKER

7 letters
JUNIPER
REDWOOD

8 letters
CHESTNUT
MAHOGANY
ROSEWOOD
SANDARAC
SYCAMORE

10 letters
EUCALYPTUS
GRANADILLA

Light Up

Place circles (representing light bulbs) in some of the empty squares, in such a way that no two bulbs shine on each other, until every square of the grid is lit up. A bulb sends rays of light horizontally and vertically, illuminating its entire row and column unless its light is blocked by a black cell.

Some black cells contain numbers, indicating how many light bulbs are in adjacent squares either immediately above, below, to the right, or to the left. Bulbs placed diagonally adjacent to a numbered cell do not contribute to the bulb count. An unnumbered black cell may have any number of light bulbs adjacent to it, or none at all, and not all light bulbs are necessarily clued via black squares.

"Mindfulness means paying attention in a particular way: on purpose, in the present moment, and non-judgmentally."

Jon Kabat-Zinn

85   Skyscrapers

Place the numbers 1 to 5 into each row and column, one number per square. Each number represents a skyscraper of that many floors.

Arrange the skyscrapers in such a way that the given number outside the grid represents the number of buildings which can be seen from that point, looking only at that number's row or column.

A skyscraper with a lower number of floors cannot hide a higher building, but a one with a higher number of floors always hides any building behind it.

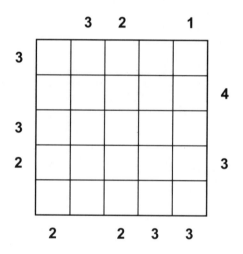

"Mindfulness is about the present, but I also think it's about being real. Being awake to everything. Feeling like nothing can hurt you if you can look it straight on."

Krista Tippett

Shadow Play

Which of the shadows is that
of the yacht shown here?

A

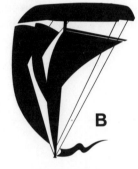

B

C

D

E

F

G

Coin Collecting

In this puzzle, an amateur coin collector has been out with his metal detector, searching for booty. He didn't have time to dig up all the coins he found, so has made a grid map, showing their locations, in the hope that if he loses the map, at least no-one else will understand it... However, he didn't count on YOU coming across the strange grid (as seen here). Will you be able to discover the correct number of coins and their precise locations?

Those squares containing numbers are empty, but where a number appears in a square, it indicates how many coins are located in the squares (up to a maximum of eight) surrounding the numbered one, touching it at any corner or side. There is only one coin in any individual square.

Place a circle into every square containing a coin.

1	2			3			1	1
	3				4		3	
2		3		5				2
	2	3		4				
		4			4		3	
						2		
3			3	4			2	
2				3				2
		2	3		4		3	

"Positive energy
is attracted to
positive energy."

Deborah Day

Sudoku

Place one of the numbers from 1 to 9 into every empty cell so that each row, each column and each 3x3 block contains all the numbers from 1 to 9.

	5		8		4			7
2	4		1				5	
			6	2			3	1
		2		3	1	6		
	1	3				8	4	
		9	4	6		3		
7	3			1	9			
	6				7		2	4
1			5		6		9	

"Open the window of
your mind. Allow the
fresh air, new lights and
new truths to enter."

Amit Ray

       # Codeword

Every letter in this puzzle has been replaced by a number, the number remaining the same for that letter wherever it occurs. Every letter of the alphabet has been used. Substitute numbers for letters to complete the codeword.

It may help to cross off the letters beneath the grid to keep a track of progress, and to use the reference box showing which numbers have been decoded. Three letters have already been entered into the grid, to help you on your way.

24	■	16	■	4	14	16	10	14	24	12	21	20	10	22
12	9	10	14	14	■	10	■	20	■	10	■	12	■	
10	■	14	■	6	12	25	18	20	1	1	14	21	21	14
4	20	4	9	14	■	26	■	19	■	1	■	25		
25	■	25	■	10	■	14	12	3	14	18	4	10	20	16
20	■	18	20	12	17	■	1	■	21	■	14	■	20	
9	12	16	■	10	■	21	■	21	■	8	12	10	6	
10	■	20	■	12	2	5	12	21	25	24	■	4	■	14
12	7	18	20	■	5	■	24	■	10	■	15	5	9	
16	■	14	■	25	■	25	■	21	5	21	5	■	10	
13	22	4	10	20	23	25	4	14	■	6	■	18	■	12
■	14	■	14	■	20	■	23	■	16	25	21	20	1	
11	12	10	11	25	21(T)	5	10	12	21	14	■	25	■	12
■	18	■	14	■	25(I)	■	7	■	21	14	1	14	21	
18	21	12	7	12	24(C)	21	25	21	14	18	■	9	■	14

A B C D E F G H I J K L M
N O P Q R S T U V W X Y Z

| 1 | 2 | 3 | 4 | 5 | 6 | 7 | 8 | 9 | 10 | 11 | 12 | 13 |
| 14 | 15 | 16 | 17 | 18 | 19 | 20 | 21 (T) | 22 | 23 | 24 (C) | 25 (I) | 26 |

Wordsearch: Authors

Can you find all of the listed words hidden in the grid below?
Words run horizontally, vertically or diagonally, in either a forward or
backward direction.

```
J  H  S  T  K  N  O  S  C  A  A  S  I  R  P
G  E  R  P  N  D  N  A  U  B  P  L  A  T  E
O  I  N  S  Y  E  L  S  G  N  I  K  A  E  A
G  R  I  M  M  G  O  L  D  S  M  I  T  H  A
T  O  R  E  D  I  D  I  Q  D  Y  P  K  R  Y
M  E  L  V  I  L  L  E  V  R  I  L  I  E  E
L  C  B  R  O  N  T  E  U  A  U  I  N  I  L
A  U  C  N  F  E  E  T  N  W  J  N  S  R  K
H  L  R  A  V  O  R  T  P  D  F  G  O  U  C
A  A  E  A  F  O  R  K  S  E  A  L  N  A  U
Y  D  N  E  W  F  C  W  S  U  A  U  F  M  B
E  S  D  O  A  V  R  C  E  A  A  C  S  U  E
E  T  E  A  T  D  A  E  R  L  C  I  O  D  Y
I  I  L  B  T  E  I  D  Y  P  L  A  E  C  X
B  S  L  G  Y  H  S  W  O  O  H  N  R  N  K
```

ARNOLD	DIDEROT	KIPLING
ATKINSON	DU MAURIER	LAHAYE
AUSTEN	EDWARDS	LUCIAN
BRONTE	EVANS	MCCAFFREY
BUCKLEY	GOLDSMITH	MELVILLE
CLEMENS	GRIMM	ORWELL
CRAIS	ISAACSON	PEACOCK
DEFOE	KINGSLEY	RENDELL

No Three in Line

Place either O or X into each empty square, so that no three consecutive squares in either a horizontal row or vertical column contain more than two of the same symbol.

There needs to be as many Os as Xs in every row and column.

		X		X	X		
O					O		
X	O		X			O	O
O	O						O
		O	O				
		X	X		X	X	
							O
	X			X			

"Ultimately, it is only
by mindfully caring for
ourselves that we can
truly and effectively
care for others with
compassion."

Arnie Kozak

Flower Power

Fit the listed words into the grid below (one letter is already in place), then rearrange the letters in the shaded squares to form another word related to the theme of this book.

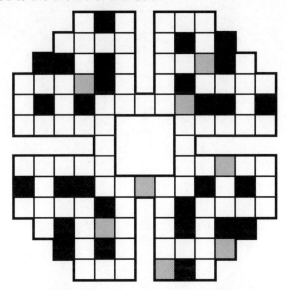

3 letters

ACE
ANY
ASP
CAP
COD
GNU
OWN
RIP

4 letters

ABET
ABLE
CHAT
CUBE
DARK
JIBE
JUMP
LAVA
MOLE
ORAL
PINT
TOOK

5 letters

ADIEU
AMBER
ANNUL
APPLE
AUGER
CHOKE
DEISM
DOYEN
EASEL
EPOCH
LATEX
RELAX

"Enlightenment is the
result of the daily practice
of mindfulness."

Shinjo Ito

Maze

Start at the top and find a path to the middle of the maze.

"Practice isn't the
thing you do once
you're good. It's the
thing you do that
makes you good."

Malcolm Gladwell

Combiku

Each horizontal row and vertical column should contain five different shapes, and five different numbers.

Every square will contain one number and one shape, and no combination may be repeated anywhere else in the puzzle; so, for instance, if a square contains a 3 and a star, then no other square containing a 3 will also contain a star, and no other square with a star will also contain a 3.

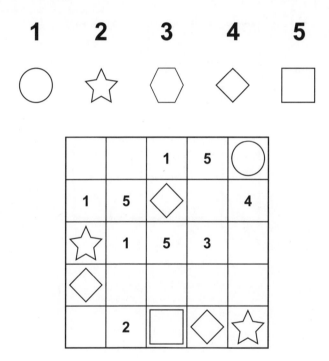

"The point of power
is always in the
present moment."

Louise Hay

Logi-5

Every row and column of this grid should contain one each of the letters A, B, C, D, and E.

In addition, each of the five shapes (marked by thicker lines) should also contain one each of the letters A, B, C, D, and E.

Can you complete the grid?

			B	C
			C	
	B			D
			E	A
	A			

"For me mindfulness is like building a house, so the next time the tsunami that is depression comes I'll have a structure in place to resist it."

Ruby Wax

Wordsearch: Floral Clock

Can you find all of the listed words hidden in the grid below?
Words run horizontally, vertically or diagonally, in either a forward or backward direction.

```
N  E  S  T  E  N  I  S  T  P  E  R  F  Y  T
A  D  E  A  L  V  C  Y  N  E  E  U  S  D  M
I  I  I  H  C  O  O  B  Z  D  V  M  I  W  C
G  N  S  R  R  Y  B  N  N  H  G  I  H  H  M
N  B  N  K  O  S  H  E  F  Q  N  N  R  S  I
I  U  A  H  R  L  V  I  L  S  I  U  U  P  A
D  R  P  A  B  A  J  T  E  I  P  T  H  I  I
N  G  A  N  L  M  P  T  V  U  A  E  O  L  R
E  H  H  D  X  R  A  A  A  F  H  S  U  U  E
T  S  E  S  S  O  M  H  R  Q  S  S  R  T  V
H  C  R  L  U  F  C  C  G  A  I  U  S  R  E
Y  R  B  H  E  J  A  M  R  L  G  E  P  P  H
M  E  S  I  L  I  O  M  A  D  D  A  O  I  C
E  F  Q  M  O  K  B  X  B  U  Y  L  I  T  E
S  E  N  E  C  I  O  J  M  J  S  U  T  N  E
```

COLEUS	LAVENDER	PRIVET
ECHEVERIA	LOBELIA	SEDUM
EDINBURGH	MCHATTIE	SENECIO
FORMAL	MINUTES	SHAPING
GRAVEL	MOSSES	SLOPE
HANDS	NIAGARA	TENDING
HERBS	PARKS	THYME
HOURS	OXALIS	TULIPS
	PANSIES	

Reflections

Which of the designs below is an exact horizontal (left to right) mirror image of the design to the right?

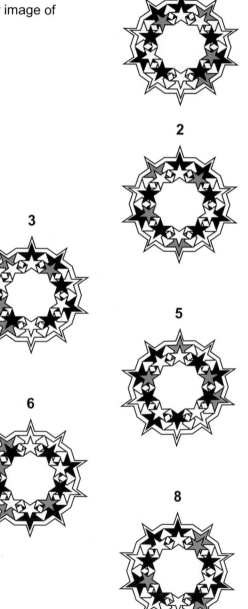

I

2

3

4

5

6

7

8

98 Coin Collecting

In this puzzle, an amateur coin collector has been out with his metal detector, searching for booty. He didn't have time to dig up all the coins he found, so has made a grid map, showing their locations, in the hope that if he loses the map, at least no-one else will understand it... However, he didn't count on YOU coming across the strange grid (as seen here). Will you be able to discover the correct number of coins and their precise locations?

Those squares containing numbers are empty, but where a number appears in a square, it indicates how many coins are located in the squares (up to a maximum of eight) surrounding the numbered one, touching it at any corner or side. There is only one coin in any individual square.

Place a circle into every square containing a coin.

1			2				
	3	3			2		1
					2	2	
2		4	4		2		1
	3					3	
	3	2	4	5			2
2			2				3
		1		2			2

"What the caterpillar calls the end of the world, the master calls a butterfly."

Richard Bach

Sudoku

Place one of the numbers from 1 to 9 into every empty cell so that each row, each column and each 3x3 block contains all the numbers from 1 to 9.

4					6			2
5	6	1				3	7	4
		3		5	1	9		
6					8	5		
	3		7		4		1	
		9	2					3
		4	6	8		2		
3	7	6				8	9	1
8			9					7

"The important thing is this:
to be able at any moment
to sacrifice what we are for
what we could become."

W E B Dubois

100

Criss Cross: Board Games

The words are provided, but can you fit them all into the grid?

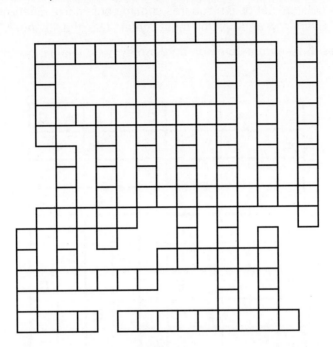

4 letters
LUDO

5 letters
CHESS
HOTEL
SORRY
TSURO

6 letters
BLOKUS
CLUEDO
MEXICA

7 letters
ACQUIRE
PATOLLI
TWISTER

8 letters
IMPERIAL
SCRABBLE

9 letters
MOUSETRAP
OBSESSION
PARCHEESI

10 letters
BATTLESHIP
SQUARE MILE

15 letters
CHINESE
   CHECKERS

Patchwork

Every square should be filled with a letter from A to E, and each heavily outlined set of five squares should contain five different letters. Every row and column must contain two of each letter.

Squares that share a common border may not contain the same letter.

D		C			C		E	A	D
E			A	C	E		A		
		B			B				C
C	B		D	A			C		A
D	A	B		D			B	A	
				B		B		C	
B		A		E					C
		E					E		
	C			E	D				
		D	E						E

"Guilt, regret, resentment, sadness and all forms of nonforgiveness are caused by too much past and not enough presence."

Eckhart Tolle

Slitherlink

Draw a single continuous loop, by connecting the dots. No line may cross the path of another.

The figure inside each set of any four surrounding dots indicates the total number of surrounding lines.

```
.   .   .   .       .   .   .   .   .   .
        3       3   1   2   3   1
.   .   .   .   .   .   .   .   .   .
 2   2   1   3   2
.   .   .   .   .   .   .   .   .   .
 1       1   2   0   2       0
.   .   .   .   .   .   .   .   .   .
 1   2   2   3       3       0
.   .   .   .   .   .   .   .   .   .
 1       2   1   1   0
.   .   .   .   .   .   .   .   .   .
 1       3       1   1       2   3
.   .   .   .   .   .   .   .   .   .
 1   1   2   1       2       0   3
.   .   .   .   .   .   .   .   .   .
         2       1   1   1   3
.   .   .   .   .   .   .   .   .   .
     2                   2
.   .   .   .   .   .   .   .   .   .
```

"I believe in not trying
to control things that
are out of my control or
none of my business."

Tobe Hanson

Wordsearch: Eating Out

Can you find all of the listed words hidden in the grid below?
Words run horizontally, vertically or diagonally, in either a forward or backward direction.

```
G A P Y S K N I R D E X A Y T
D N E S U O H K A E T S T E J
S E I Y R E L T U C N R L E R
A D S P H E R N L P A I L F N
R E R R P A M A T P R Y D F X
E G E H U I Y R R S R E V O C
P B T B X O T U E S R G S C N
P D I T A A C A S U A L E J I
U E A S B R T T S R T O S C K
S P W L T S B S E P E N S C P
S S E A H R D E D E A S A A A
G U P F O M O R C R W R L V N
B A S N O E H C N U L S G L E
S H Y H H O R S D O E U V R E
N E M F I N A I R A T E G E V
```

BARBECUE

BISTRO

COFFEE

COVERS

CUTLERY

DESSERT

DINER

DRINKS

GLASSES

HORS D'OEUVRE

LUNCHEON

NAPKIN

PARTY

RESTAURANT

SEATS

STEAKHOUSE

SUPPER

SUSHI

SWEET COURSE

TABLE

TAPAS

TIPPING

VEGETARIAN

WAITER

104 Combiku

Each horizontal row and vertical column should contain five different shapes, and five different numbers.

Every square will contain one number and one shape, and no combination may be repeated anywhere else in the puzzle; so, for instance, if a square contains a 3 and a star, then no other square containing a 3 will also contain a star, and no other square with a star will also contain a 3.

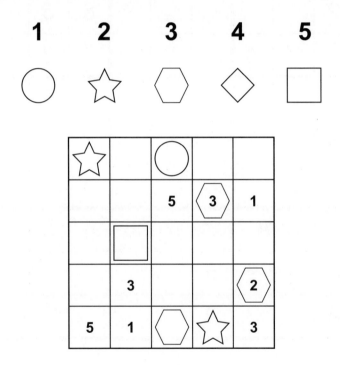

"It's not so much that we're afraid of change or so in love with the old ways, but it's that place in between that we fear. It's like being between trapezes."

Marilyn Ferguson

Sudoku

Place one of the numbers from 1 to 9 into every empty cell so that each row, each column and each 3x3 block contains all the numbers from 1 to 9.

					2			4
2					7	8	5	
	7	4	1	3			2	
	9	2			4	5	6	
3				6				7
	6	1	8			3	9	
	3			2	6	4	8	
	4	9	5					1
8			9					

"The only way to make sense out of change is to plunge into it, move with it, and join the dance."

Alan Watts

Codeword

Every letter in this puzzle has been replaced by a number, the number remaining the same for that letter wherever it occurs. Every letter of the alphabet has been used. Substitute numbers for letters to complete the codeword.

It may help to cross off the letters beneath the grid to keep a track of progress, and to use the reference box showing which numbers have been decoded. Three letters have already been entered into the grid, to help you on your way.

17	10	5	4	24	4	■	4	21	3	16	4	6	4	24
10	■	21	■	4	■	■	■	3	■	1	■	16	■	17
9	12	9	4	10	17	3	■	9 A	■	10	4	4	26	21
15	■	23	■	18	■	23	17	10 M	19	1	■	20	■	5
17	10	10	4	20	21	4	■	5 P	■	12	17	4	3	4
12	■	■	24	■	4	7	7	17	15	2	■	17	■	23
4	25	3	17	21	4	■	20	■	9	10	4	12	■	■
24	■	■	3	■	21	8	18	17	24	■	23	■	■	21
■	21	26	1	9	■	■	17	■	15	18	7	7	9	6
11	■	14	■	21	6	9	26	16	4	■	17	■	■	4
9	25	17	1	10	■	13	■	18	26	4	12	21	17	23
22	■	12	■	1	3	4	9	12	■	12	■	6	■	26
22	1	12	4	21	■	12	■	15	20	4	12	9	24	4
4	■	4	■	17	■	15	■	■	10	■	10	■	■	20
21	17	24	4	21	26	4	5	■	3	9	10	5	18	21

A B C D E F G H I J K L M

N O P Q R S T U V W X Y Z

1	2	3	4	5 P	6	7	8	9 A	10 M	11	12	13
14	15	16	17	18	19	20	21	22	23	24	25	26

107   Pyragram

Every clue in this puzzle is an anagram leading to a single-word solution. Correctly solve the anagram on each level of the pyramid and another word will appear, reading down the central column.

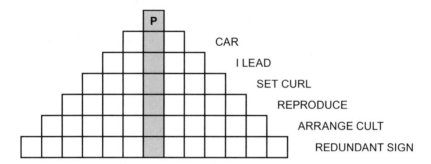

CAR

I LEAD

SET CURL

REPRODUCE

ARRANGE CULT

REDUNDANT SIGN

108   Word Wheel

How many words of three or more letters can you make from those in the wheel, without using plurals, abbreviations or proper nouns?

The central letter must appear once in every word and no letter in a section of the wheel may be used more than once.

There is at least one nine-letter word in the wheel.

Nine-letter word(s):

_____

Criss Cross: Horse Breeds

The words are provided, but can you fit them all into the grid?

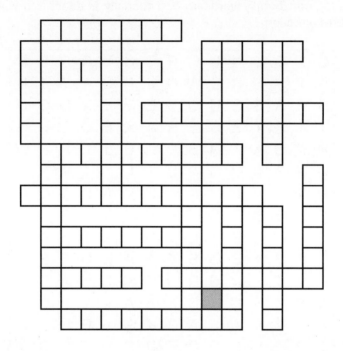

5 letters
IOMUD
MOYLE
SHIRE

6 letters
LOSINO
MISAKI
MIYAKO
MORGAN

7 letters
ARABIAN
HACKNEY
SUFFOLK

8 letters
ASTURIAN
BALEARIC
LUSITANO

9 letters
FINNHORSE
GRONINGEN
MONGOLIAN
OLDENBURG

10 letters
BHIRUM PONY

12 letters
CLEVELAND BAY

Wordsearch: In the Park

Can you find all of the listed words hidden in the grid below?
Words run horizontally, vertically or diagonally, in either a forward or
backward direction.

```
C  I  S  D  N  U  O  R  O  G  Y  R  R  E  M
B  Y  S  S  R  E  W  O  L  F  U  A  G  Z  D
S  A  A  B  S  U  O  B  E  M  E  N  D  O  D
T  I  R  T  E  S  E  R  A  K  E  O  D  N  G
R  P  G  A  I  N  B  P  N  U  J  L  R  N  W
O  X  B  N  C  Q  G  U  T  L  T  I  I  P  T
P  S  N  H  L  V  K  A  R  V  A  K  T  Q  E
S  E  E  R  T  S  T  K  V  H  L  C  S  K  A
T  S  T  H  E  S  E  T  S  A  S  I  H  D  D
E  E  B  A  S  G  S  E  W  A  E  N  T  B  U
C  T  T  S  W  U  R  N  S  M  L  C  A  P  C
N  S  B  S  E  F  B  F  A  A  V  I  P  O  K
E  T  G  E  A  S  A  Z  K  W  Z  P  R  N  S
F  O  E  E  L  P  O  E  P  E  S  T  O  D  I
D  Z  G  S  L  E  R  R  I  U  Q  S  V  S  L
```

BENCHES	LAKE	SHRUBS
BUSHES	MERRY-GO-	SPORTS
DOGS	ROUND	SQUIRRELS
DUCKS	PATHS	STATUE
FENCE	PEOPLE	SWANS
FLOWERS	PICNIC	TENNIS
FRESH AIR	PONDS	TREES
GRASS	ROSES	WALKING
	SEATS	

Calcudoku

Each row and column should contain different numbers from 1 to 6.

The numbers placed in a heavily outlined set of squares may be repeated, but must produce the calculation in the top left corner, using the mathematical symbol provided: multiply (x), divide (/), add (+), and subtract (−).

For example, when multiplied, the numbers 4 and 3 total 12:

12x	
4	**3**

18+			3/	120x	
	7+	10+			
24x			4/		4+
	15x		4−		
	6+	1−	150x	48x	

"Spread love everywhere you go. Let no one ever come to you without leaving happier."

Mother Teresa

Bridges

Join the circular islands by drawing horizontal or vertical lines to represent bridges, in such a way that the number of bridges connected to each island must match the number on that island. No bridge may cross another, and no more than two bridges can join any pair of islands.

The finished design will allow you to travel from one island to any other island on the map.

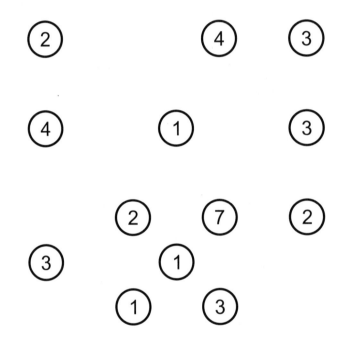

"**There is no better means of attainment to the spiritual life than by continually beginning again.**"

St Francis de Sales

113   Wordsearch: Flower Arranging

Can you find all of the listed words hidden in the grid below?
Words run horizontally, vertically or diagonally, in either a forward or
backward direction.

```
A R E G N O P S L L E H S H A
E C C A H S Y G B A S K E T R
N G O R O E S A N F A S T W E
M P R R U I Z E G I S D E T B
P A S E S O R W I E T T F C R
W F O O E A S A A R S T E F E
Y I V F P N G T U L R O U M G
A X R V L G E E R E P E N C S
L S L I A A N R B V E A B L R
P C N X N K R O Y A B B E R Y
S H H O T G U O U R B I M A J
I N A Z B Q U E L G L N R F P
D P R Y U B A R E F E P D O H
S E B E A L I H P O S P Y G I
U R T A F A T R O P P U S K I
```

BASKET	GERBERA	ROSES
BERRIES	GRAVEL	SHELLS
BOUQUET	GREENERY	SPONGE
CORSAGE	GYPSOPHILA	SPRAY
CUTTING	HOUSE PLANT	STEMS
DISPLAY	NOSEGAY	SUPPORT
FERNS	PEBBLES	WATER
FLORAL FOAM	RIBBONS	WIRING

Sudoku

Place one of the numbers from 1 to 9 into every empty cell so that each row, each column and each 3x3 block contains all the numbers from 1 to 9.

	7				4	5	6	
				1	7	2		
8	9	4						1
4			5	3		6		2
		8	6		9	1		
5		9		4	2			7
1						8	2	3
		2	4	5				
	3	6	8				7	

"The passing moment is all that we can be sure of; it is only common sense to extract its utmost value from it."

W. Somerset Maugham

Codeword

Every letter in this puzzle has been replaced by a number, the number remaining the same for that letter wherever it occurs. Every letter of the alphabet has been used. Substitute numbers for letters to complete the codeword.

It may help to cross off the letters beneath the grid to keep a track of progress, and to use the reference box showing which numbers have been decoded. Three letters have already been entered into the grid, to help you on your way.

13	23	8	23	16	3		17	4	7	4	13	4	8	4
4		22		25		25		5		14		12		22
17	4	8	25	13		11	12	5	13	11	12	19	23	14
1		11		25	15	9		11		23		23		11
9 L	11 I	3 T		12		2	23	20	3	22	21	9	23	3
23		2		23			12		22		25		17	
2	18	22	4	13	11	2	7		1	4	9	2	4	17
	22		13		12		4		23		11		11	
16	4	13	23	2	2		12	4	13	13	25	15	9	6
	24		12		23		16			4		4		23
21	23	12	4	9	3	11	23	2		17		19	23	9
9		25		11		2		25	14	23		3		9
4	14	10	25	16	4	3	23	14		24	7	4	24	11
26		23		11		9		4		11		11		12
4	9	9	25	3	3	23	14		22	12	16	9	25	19

A B C D E F G H I J K L M

N O P Q R S T U V W X Y Z

1	2	3 T	4	5	6	7	8	9 L	10	11 I	12	13
14	15	16	17	18	19	20	21	22	23	24	25	26

Wordsearch: Children

Can you find all of the listed words hidden in the grid below?
Words run horizontally, vertically or diagonally, in either a forward or backward direction.

```
T N A F N I G N I R P S F F O
M L E F H L P E B A E T F C S
A Y Y T K U A Y L A S S I E H
R O U O P Y N V P O I T C M A
I O N I U E L C S H O R A G V
Y A L I G N M G H T M E N D E
B H A O B I G E T I U A Z D R
V D R N U M A O N O A D M T R
R P E O R P A O N I T G E A D
E Z G S E T R B E E H Y S N U
L B A P H E I D D A L C N B T
D T N E C S E L O D A R R I E
D F E T S A I A N L M W E U T
O R E S T H D E L I N E V U J
T C T T C R E T S G N U O Y A
```

ADOLESCENT	LASSIE	STUDENT
BAIRN	MINOR	TEENAGER
BAMBINO	OFFSPRING	TINY TOT
CHERUB	PROGENY	TODDLER
CHILD	PUPIL	URCHIN
INFANT	RASCAL	YOUNG ONE
JUVENILE	SHAVER	YOUNGSTER
LADDIE	STEPSON	YOUTH

Criss Cross: Affirm

The words are provided, but can you fit them all into the grid?

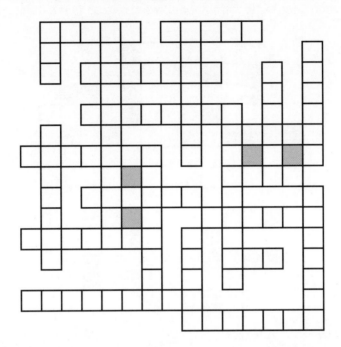

3 letters
SAY
VOW

4 letters
AVER

5 letters
AGREE
STATE
SWEAR
VOUCH

6 letters
ALLEGE
ASSERT
PLEDGE
RATIFY

7 letters
CONFIRM
CONFORM
DECLARE
ENDORSE
PROFESS
PROTEST
TESTIFY

8 letters
MAINTAIN
POSITIVE

9 letters
ESTABLISH
PRONOUNCE

11 letters
CORROBORATE

Flower Power

Fit the listed words into the grid below, then rearrange the letters in the shaded squares to form another word related to the theme of this book.

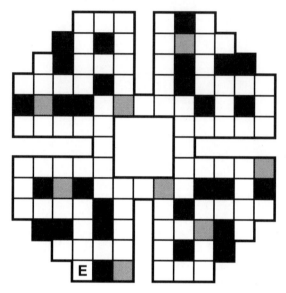

3 letters
AIL
GYM
LET
NET
PEW
PUN
RUM
WIG

4 letters
ABUT
AMEN
AWRY
CUBA
DIAL
DIVE

GALE
LORD
LYRE
TWIN
WILL
WREN

5 letters
CHIEF
CRISP
FLOSS
FLUSH
LEANT
MOTOR

PEACE
PRESS
RIGHT
SCANS
SCRAP
SKULL

"Stop, breathe, look around
and embrace the miracle of
each day, the miracle of life."

Jeffrey A White

No Four in Line

Place either O or X into each empty square, so that no four consecutive squares in a straight line in any direction (horizontally, vertically, or diagonally) contain more than three of the same symbol.

X	X			O		O	O	X
X			X			O		O
O						X	O	X
	X						X	
X				O				X
X	X							X
X			X	X	X		X	
	O			X			O	X
X	X		X	X			O	O

"Feelings, whether of
compassion or irritation,
should be welcomed,
recognized, and treated
on an absolutely equal
basis; because both
are ourselves."

Thich Nhat Hanh

120   Pyragram

Every clue in this puzzle is an anagram leading to a single-word solution. Correctly solve the anagram on each level of the pyramid and another word will appear, reading down the central column.

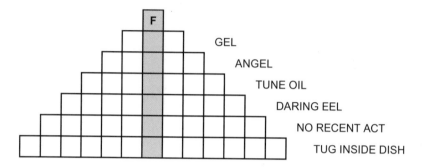

GEL
ANGEL
TUNE OIL
DARING EEL
NO RECENT ACT
TUG INSIDE DISH

121   Word Ladder

Change one letter at a time (but not the position of any letter) to make a new word – and move from the word at the top of the ladder to the word at the bottom using the exact number of rungs provided.

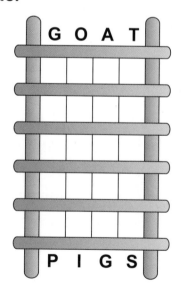

Sudoku

Place one of the numbers from 1 to 9 into every empty cell so that each row, each column and each 3x3 block contains all the numbers from 1 to 9.

		7	8		2	5		
9				7				6
	2	5	1		6	7	4	
2			5	8	7			1
	7	4				3	8	
1			2	4	3			7
	1	2	3		8	9	6	
8				2				5
		9	7		4	8		

"Mindfulness helps you go home
to the present. And every time
you go there and recognize
a condition of happiness that
you have, happiness comes."

Thich Nhat Hanh

123   Wordsearch:
Hope

Can you find all of the underlined words from the poem "Hope"
by Emily Dickinson? Words run forward or backward, in either a
horizontal, vertical, or diagonal direction.

```
B  T  S  E  L  L  I  H  C  E  S  U  N
M  A  Y  S  S  E  H  C  R  E  P  D  A
U  E  T  S  G  E  A  R  A  O  N  O  I
R  A  I  D  T  N  U  H  S  A  B  A  H
C  L  M  R  D  F  I  P  L  S  O  U  L
E  E  E  O  W  R  E  H  L  P  N  W  T
N  S  R  W  S  S  A  I  T  E  Q  P  T
U  R  T  T  O  W  T  E  V  R  E  D  S
T  E  X  R  S  T  E  E  H  K  O  E  E
S  H  E  E  L  U  R  E  N  D  U  K  G
T  T  M  E  C  B  M  L  T  E  L  S  N
O  A  O  R  I  O  Y  A  W  E  I  A  A
P  E  O  R  A  P  U  G  N  N  S  F  R
S  F  D  R  M  W  F  L  G  Y  H  T  T
T  U  O  H  T  I  W  S  D  A  F  E  S
```

Hope is the thing with feathers
That perches in the soul,
And sings the tune without the words,
And never stops at all.

And sweetest in the gale is heard;
And sore must be the storm
That could abash the little bird
That kept so many warm.

I've heard it in the chillest land,
And on the strangest sea;
Yet, never, in extremity,
It asked a crumb of me.

Codeword

Every letter in this puzzle has been replaced by a number, the number remaining the same for that letter wherever it occurs. Every letter of the alphabet has been used. Substitute numbers for letters to complete the codeword.

It may help to cross off the letters beneath the grid to keep a track of progress, and to use the reference box showing which numbers have been decoded. Three letters have already been entered into the grid, to help you on your way.

17	25	26	26	3	7		25	17	5	23	20	7	4	23
11		5		25				5		11		25 A		5
23	7	4	5	22	7	16		22		10	25	22 R	7	22
6		24		24		7	9	7	22	21		20 M		22
7	10	15	23	11	20	7		25		15	20	25	24	7
22			6		15	20	17	5	7	16		22		23
7	8	14	7	10	23		3		4	7	14	1		
16			23		23	15	25	22	25		22			10
		14	25	10	7		18		17	3	11	23	14	6
12		25		5	4	22	7	25	3		14			25
5	23	23	7	22		7		13	7	22	1	15	7	22
25		7		2	15	3	3	25		7		21		20
14	11	22	24	15		15		22	15	14	11	23	23	25
1		7		7		2				23		3		14
21	10	22	25	9	3	7	22		10	11	10	7	22	19

A B C D E F G H I J K L M
N O P Q R S T U V W X Y Z

1	2	3	4	5	6	7	8	9	10	11	12	13
14	15	16	17	18	19	20 M	21	22 R	23	24	25 A	26

Sudoku

Place one of the numbers from 1 to 9 into every empty cell so that each row, each column and each 3x3 block contains all the numbers from 1 to 9.

6		4	3		2	5		
5			6		7	8		
	8			9				1
		1			5		2	6
		7		3		4		
9	4		8			3		
4				7			5	
		8	4		1			2
		9	2		3	7		8

"It is only possible to live
happily-ever-after on
a day-to-day basis."

Margaret Wander Bonnano

126 Criss Cross: Better and Better

The words are provided, but can you fit them all into the grid?

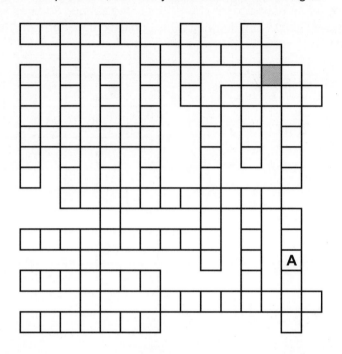

4 letters	**7 letters**	**9 letters**
WELL	GREATER	A CUT ABOVE
	REVISED	TOUCHED UP
5 letters	SMARTER	
FINER	SOUNDER	**10 letters**
NICER	SWEETER	PREFERABLE
6 letters	**8 letters**	**11 letters**
FITTER	POLISHED	PROGRESSING
HEALED	REFORMED	
LARGER	SUPERIOR	
MENDED		
NEATER		

In Place

Place the listed words horizontally into the grid, so that when read from top left to bottom right, the letters in the shaded squares spell out a word linked to the theme of this book. Some letters are already in place.

ATTUNED

BENEFIT

COMPACT

GREATER

MAXIMUM

SOMEONE

WELFARE

		N				
				M		
		M				
				O		

"Mindfulness requires that we not over-identify with thoughts and feelings so that we are caught up and swept away by negativity."

Brené Brown

128   **Maze**

Start at the top and find a path to the middle of the maze.

"Once you replace
negative thoughts with
positive ones, you'll start
having positive results."

Willie Nelson

129 Wordsearch: Herbal Remedies

Can you find all of the listed words hidden in the grid below?
Words run horizontally, vertically or diagonally, in either a forward or
backward direction.

```
G A R L E A S T R E M O R K O
A W O L L A M H S R A M C R Y
L A R E G N I G H U A U R J E
A L O E V E R A P S N I U A R
N L E G N G O Y L I S D H D F
G E B U K L A A R K L E E K M
A G V O K N B R C A A S N W O
L M I V R U I O L R M P W N C
U H O N N A L G T I A E A O A
S U L I S M G S I R C T S X C
A B E O E E E S A F F R O N
T A T H V A N L E N E R A S R
F S M D S A E G L E R R O S Y
E I A E J Y G O L D E N R O D
N L I N E R I E H E P T R I D
```

ALOE VERA	GINGER	ORRIS
BALSAM	GINKGO	PARSLEY
BASIL	GINSENG	ROSEMARY
BORAGE	GOLDENROD	SAFFRON
COMFREY	HEARTSEASE	SENNA
COWSLIP	HEMLOCK	SORREL
GALANGAL	LOVAGE	SUNDEW
GARLIC	MARSH- MALLOW	VIOLET

Futoshiki

Fill the grid so that every horizontal row and vertical column contains all the numbers 1 to 7.

Any arrows in the grid always point toward a square that contains a lower number.

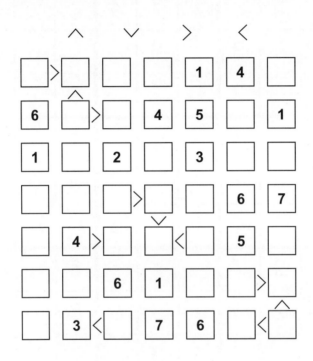

"Wanderer, your footsteps
are the road, and nothing
more; wanderer, there
is no road, the road is
made by walking."

Antonio Machado

Sudoku

Place one of the numbers from 1 to 9 into every empty cell so that each row, each column and each 3x3 block contains all the numbers from 1 to 9.

8	5			7	4			
1		3		8			6	
6		2				9	7	
9			3			1		
	6	1	7		8	3	5	
		4			5			2
	9	7				5		4
	2			3		8		1
			4	9			3	6

"To escape the self-trap,
to be sane and decent
and awake and whole –
that is all that matters."

Vernon Howard

Domino Placement

A standard set of 28 dominoes has been laid out as shown. Can you draw in the edges of them all?

The check-box is provided as an aid, so that you can see which dominoes have been located.

3	3	1	4	6	0	1
4	2	2	3	4	3	1
0	0	6	5	6	2	3
1	0	4	4	6	4	0
0	4	2	6	1	6	4
2	2	6	3	3	0	5
5	1	2	0	5	2	5
3	1	6	5	5	1	5

0-0	0-1	0-2	0-3	0-4	0-5	0-6	1-1	1-2	1-3	1-4	1-5	1-6	2-2

2-3	2-4	2-5	2-6	3-3	3-4	3-5	3-6	4-4	4-5	4-6	5-5	5-6	6-6
										✓			

"Mindfulness is awareness
without comment,
without discrimination,
without judgment."

Steven Harrison

133   Jigsaw

Which four shapes (two black and two white) can be fitted together to form the hummingbird shown here? The pieces may be rotated, but not flipped over.

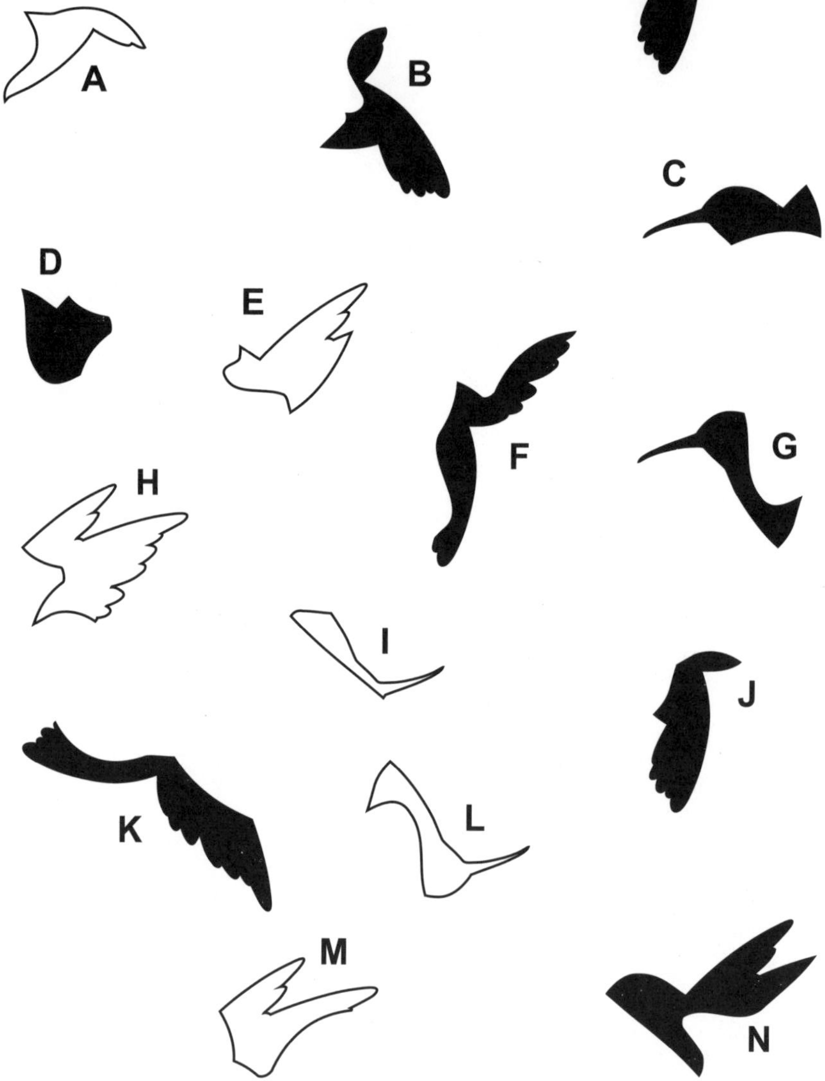

A

B

C

D

E

F

G

H

I

J

K

L

M

N

134   Criss Cross: In Our Dreams

The words are provided, but can you fit them all into the grid?

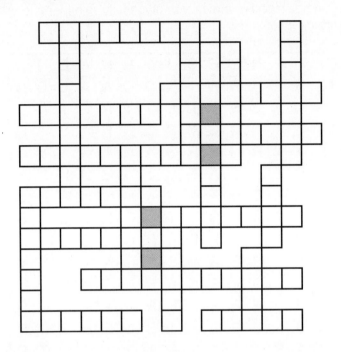

4 letters
FOOD
HOME
WORK

5 letters
SHEEP

6 letters
FAMILY
FLYING
SCHOOL

7 letters
ANIMALS
CASTLES
COFFINS
FALLING
FLOWERS
IRONING
THE PAST
THE WIFE

8 letters
FOOTBALL
SWIMMING

9 letters
CHOCOLATE
HAPPINESS
THE FUTURE

11 letters
GETTING LOST

Wordsearch: Train Ride

Can you find all of the listed words hidden in the grid below?
Words run horizontally, vertically or diagonally, in either a forward or
backward direction.

```
Y R E N E C S J M R N W E N D
G A E Y F W I N D O W A L E O
S N A E S I L E J T R E T A F
A O I N C S Y P E C R A S R H
K A T R H E R S A U T G I Y G
A R E U E A E V T D M D H L N
E R K O D T A R K N O H W P S
P I C J U S A T M O R A L I S
F V I L L P R C R C E C J I Z
F A T E E A M S Y O N T G K M
O L E D V B U F F E T N U L T
L H F E R E S E R V A T I O N
W U L U G G E L S L E E P E R
E A S S A L C T S R I F S Z Q
R B E N I G N E L U G G A G E
```

ARRIVAL	JOURNEY	SEATS
BUFFET	LUGGAGE	SIGNALS
CATERING	OFF-PEAK	SLEEPER
CONDUCTOR	RAILS	TICKET
DEPARTURE	RESERVATION	TRAVEL
DOORS	ROUTE	WHEELS
ENGINE	SCENERY	WHISTLE
FIRST CLASS	SCHEDULE	WINDOW

Number Link

Working from one square to another, horizontally or vertically (never diagonally), draw single continuous paths to pair up each set of two matching numbers.

No line may cross another, none may travel through any square containing a number, and every square must be visited just once.

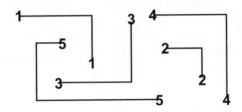

		12	11					8
12		1	10					3
	15			8		16		
1	15		11	2		3	4	
9	10		7			18		
	9				18	6		
7			13					16
				14				4
	5	17			2			6
17	5	13						14

"Passion is energy. Feel the power that comes from focusing on what excites you."

Oprah Winfrey

137   Pyragram

Every clue in this puzzle is an anagram leading to a single-word solution. Correctly solve the anagram on each level of the pyramid and another word will appear, reading down the central column.

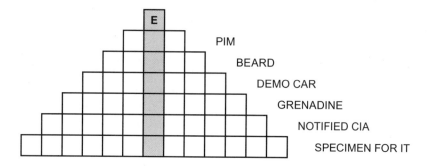

PIM

BEARD

DEMO CAR

GRENADINE

NOTIFIED CIA

SPECIMEN FOR IT

138   Word Wheel

How many words of three or more letters can you make from those in the wheel, without using plurals, abbreviations or proper nouns?

The central letter must appear once in every word and no letter in a section of the wheel may be used more than once.

There is at least one nine-letter word in the wheel.

Nine-letter word(s):

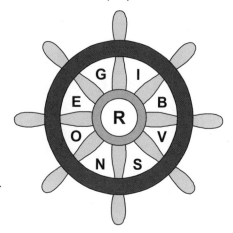

139   Codeword

Every letter in this puzzle has been replaced by a number, the number remaining the same for that letter wherever it occurs. Every letter of the alphabet has been used. Substitute numbers for letters to complete the codeword.

It may help to cross off the letters beneath the grid to keep a track of progress, and to use the reference box showing which numbers have been decoded. Three letters have already been entered into the grid, to help you on your way.

20		7		13	16	25	10	6	16	10	5	23	18	10
10	5	8	10	20		18			19		13		13	
2		10		7	21 H	5 A	16 M	10	18	10	7	7	18	15
4	21	5	4	13		9			18		18		5	
10		16		3		5	2	26	11	13	10	7	2	10
6		6	10	20	8		21		7			21		1
2	19	19		13			10		4		7	19	24	5
21		18		5	8	21	10	13	7	8		12		3
13	7	18	10		13		8			6		17	11	3
10		10			8		5		16	10	20	11		10
24	19	6	8	20	13	3	21	8		5		16		6
	22		11		22			6		7	10	25	13	5
25	19	6	8	16	5	20	8	10	5	11		13		8
	18		19		8			10		6	5	20	3	10
2	19	11	6	8	10	19	11	7	18	15		3		14

A B C D E F G H I J K L M

N O P Q R S T U V W X Y Z

1	2	3	4	5 A	6	7	8	9	10	11	12	13
14	15	16 M	17	18	19	20	21 H	22	23	24	25	26

Sudoku

Place one of the numbers from 1 to 9 into every empty cell so that each row, each column and each 3x3 block contains all the numbers from 1 to 9.

		7		9		3		
	1	4			7	9	2	
9		5	6			7		1
			8	3			6	7
4								2
5	7			1	2			
6		9			4	2		8
	8	1	9			5	3	
		3		5		6		

"We cannot live in the past; it is gone. Nor can we live in the future; it is forever beyond our grasp. We can live only in the present."

S.N. Goenka

Solutions

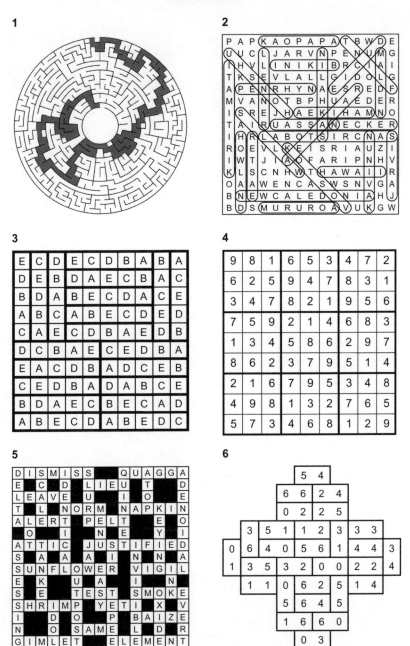

Solutions

7

8

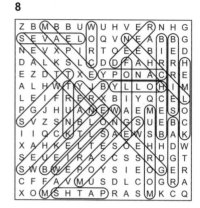

9

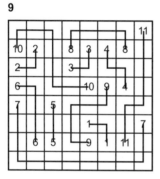

10

11
The nine-letter word is:
RECEPTIVE

12

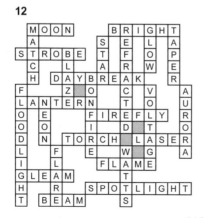

13

8	7	2	5	9	4	3	6	1
3	9	4	1	6	7	5	2	8
1	6	5	2	3	8	7	4	9
4	5	8	9	2	3	1	7	6
2	3	6	7	1	5	8	9	4
9	1	7	8	4	6	2	3	5
7	2	9	4	5	1	6	8	3
5	4	3	6	8	2	9	1	7
6	8	1	3	7	9	4	5	2

Solutions

14

15

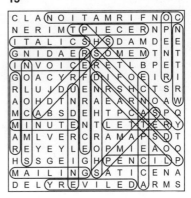

16

17

Answer: PEACEFUL

18

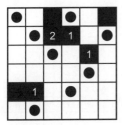

19

8	7	1	5	2	9	6	4	3
4	9	6	1	3	8	7	5	2
3	5	2	7	6	4	1	8	9
5	2	4	3	8	1	9	6	7
1	3	8	6	9	7	4	2	5
7	6	9	4	5	2	8	3	1
9	1	3	8	4	5	2	7	6
6	4	7	2	1	3	5	9	8
2	8	5	9	7	6	3	1	4

Solutions

20

21

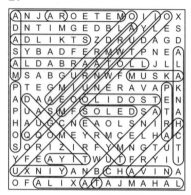

22

23

24

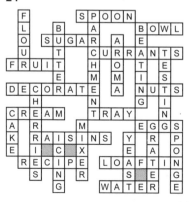

25

				H				
			D	E	W			
		S	K	A	T	E		
	D	A	R	L	I	N	G	
C	A	N	D	I	D	A	T	E
R	E	S	P	O	N	S	I	B	L	E
C	H	O	R	E	O	G	R	A	P	H	E	R

26

LAKE - make - male - pale - pole -
poll - POOL
(Other solutions are possible)

Solutions

27

5	1	2	4	3
4	3	1	2	5
2	5	3	1	4
3	2	4	5	1
1	4	5	3	2

28

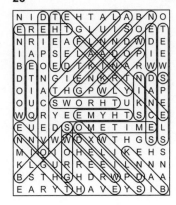

29

O	O	X	O	X	O	X	X
O	O	X	O	X	O	X	X
X	X	O	X	O	X	O	O
O	O	X	X	O	X	X	O
X	X	O	O	X	O	O	X
O	O	X	O	X	O	X	X
X	X	O	X	O	X	O	O
X	X	O	X	O	X	O	O

30

5	6	7	4	3	2	1	9	8
3	1	2	9	7	8	4	5	6
9	4	8	1	6	5	3	2	7
6	9	5	3	8	7	2	1	4
1	8	3	6	2	4	5	7	9
2	7	4	5	1	9	8	6	3
8	5	1	7	4	6	9	3	2
4	3	6	2	9	1	7	8	5
7	2	9	8	5	3	6	4	1

31

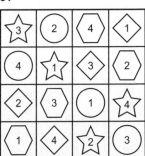

32

D

Solutions

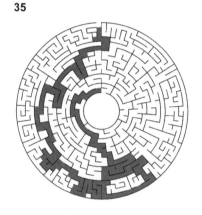

36

D	A	C	E	B
B	C	D	A	E
A	E	B	C	D
E	B	A	D	C
C	D	E	B	A

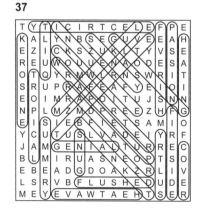

38

4	9	5	2	1	7	3	6	8
7	2	6	8	9	3	5	4	1
8	3	1	5	4	6	2	7	9
3	8	7	6	2	4	1	9	5
1	6	9	7	8	5	4	3	2
2	5	4	9	3	1	7	8	6
9	4	2	3	5	8	6	1	7
5	7	3	1	6	9	8	2	4
6	1	8	4	7	2	9	5	3

Solutions

39

40

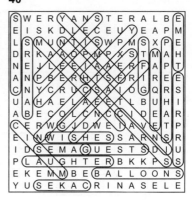

41

1	1	2		2	1		1
2	●		●	4	●	4	●
2	●		2	●	●	●	2
	3	2			5	5	
●	2	●	1	1	●	●	●
2				2	5		●
●	2			1	2	3	●
2	●			●		●	2

42

Answer: SIMPLICITY

43

B	A	D	A	C	B	D	C
A	C	B	D	A	C	B	D
C	D	A	B	C	D	A	B
D	B	D	C	B	A	C	A
B	A	C	B	D	C	A	D
A	D	B	C	A	D	B	C
D	C	A	D	B	A	C	B
C	B	C	A	D	B	D	A

44

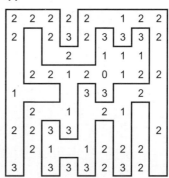

Solutions

45

8	4	7	6	5	2	3	1	9
5	1	9	8	3	4	2	7	6
6	3	2	1	9	7	8	4	5
9	2	1	7	8	5	6	3	4
3	8	6	4	2	1	5	9	7
4	7	5	3	6	9	1	8	2
1	9	8	5	4	6	7	2	3
2	6	3	9	7	8	4	5	1
7	5	4	2	1	3	9	6	8

46

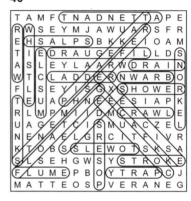

47

T	R	E	N	C	H		V	A	S	T	N	E	S	S
R		L		I		Y		T		R		X		U
E	J	E	C	T		O	U	T	F	O	X	I	N	G
E		G		I	N	K		I		L		S		A
T	E	A		Z		E	S	C	A	L	A	T	O	R
O		N		E		E		P		M		N		
P	A	T	E	N	T	E	D		R	A	B	B	I	T
	D		N		E		U		O		E		O	
W	O	O	D	E	N		C	O	N	F	R	O	N	T
	R		O		E		E		O		V		R	
S	N	O	W	S	T	O	R	M		U		E	Y	E
Q		A		C		F		O	W	N		R		A
U	N	K	N	O	T	T	E	D		D	R	E	A	D
I		E		W		E		E		E		A		L
B	U	N	G	L	I	N	G		W	R	I	T	H	E

48

5	4	7	6	3	2	9	8	1
2	1	8	9	7	5	6	4	3
9	6	3	1	4	8	7	2	5
8	3	1	7	6	9	4	5	2
6	5	2	3	8	4	1	9	7
4	7	9	2	5	1	8	3	6
7	9	5	8	2	6	3	1	4
3	8	4	5	1	7	2	6	9
1	2	6	4	9	3	5	7	8

49

(crossword grid)

50

4	1	2	3	6	5
6	3	5	2	1	4
5	4	3	6	2	1
3	6	1	5	4	2
1	2	6	4	5	3
2	5	4	1	3	6

Solutions

51

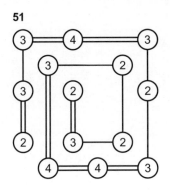

52

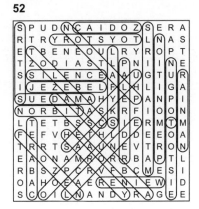

53

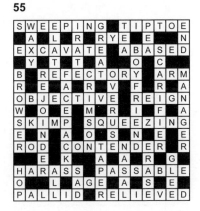

54

9	5	8	1	6	2	4	7	3
1	2	4	3	9	7	6	8	5
3	6	7	5	4	8	1	9	2
4	1	6	2	8	5	9	3	7
7	9	5	6	1	3	2	4	8
2	8	3	9	7	4	5	6	1
8	4	1	7	2	9	3	5	6
6	3	9	8	5	1	7	2	4
5	7	2	4	3	6	8	1	9

55

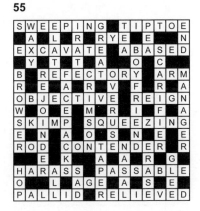

56

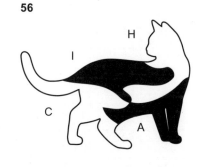

147

Solutions

57

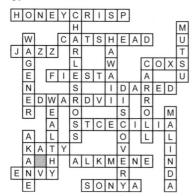

58

59

O	X	X	O	X	O	O	O	X
X	O	O	O	X	X	O	O	O
X	X	O	X	O	X	O	O	X
O	X	X	O	O	X	X	O	X
X	O	O	O	X	O	X	O	X
X	O	O	X	O	O	X	O	O
O	X	X	X	O	X	O	X	X
O	O	X	X	X	O	O	X	X
X	O	X	O	X	O	X	X	X

60

61

The nine-letter word is:
EASYGOING

62

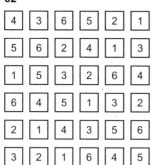

63

3	9	8	1	4	7	2	5	6
5	1	2	6	9	3	7	8	4
4	6	7	5	8	2	3	1	9
2	7	5	9	3	4	8	6	1
8	3	9	2	1	6	5	4	7
1	4	6	8	7	5	9	3	2
7	5	1	3	6	9	4	2	8
6	2	4	7	5	8	1	9	3
9	8	3	4	2	1	6	7	5

Solutions

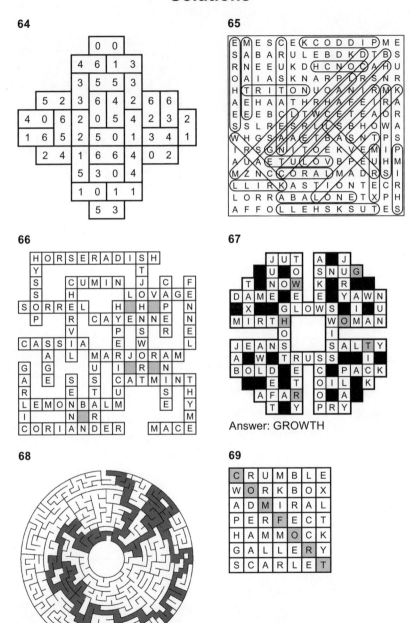

64

65

66

67

Answer: GROWTH

68

69

149

Solutions

70

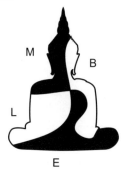

M

B

L

E

71

72

F	L	Y	I	N	G		A		Y		B	O	Y	S
L		O		E		O	R	M	O	L	U			Y
U	N	D	E	R	C	U	T		G		B	E	A	R
F		E		V		Z		I	A	M	B			I
F	A	L	S	E	H	O	O	D			L	A	W	N
V			O			O	G	R	E		G			G
R	A	M	S	H	A	C	K	L	E		G	A	T	E
	I		E		X		I	N		U		U		
P	L	U	M		E	M	P	L	O	Y	M	E	N	T
I		A	W	R	Y			M						I
Q	U	I	P			T	O	L	E	R	A	N	C	E
U		H	U	S	H		I		U		O			N
A	L	T	O		I		J	A	I	L	B	I	R	D
N			R	A	T	H	E	R		E		S		E
T	A	K	E		E		T		F	R	I	E	N	D

73

2	8	1	7	5	3	4	9	6
5	9	3	4	6	8	7	1	2
7	6	4	2	9	1	8	3	5
8	7	5	9	1	2	6	4	3
3	4	6	5	8	7	9	2	1
1	2	9	3	4	6	5	7	8
4	1	8	6	2	9	3	5	7
9	3	2	8	7	5	1	6	4
6	5	7	1	3	4	2	8	9

74

(crossword grid: BESTMAN, TIARA, CAMERA, ROSES, RINGS, SERVICE, CONFETTI, CEREMONY, GARTER, HUSBAND, WIFE, DRESS, VOWS, PAGES)

75

(pyramid: C / THE / TEACH / IMPRESS / CONTINUAL / CONDITIONER / MOTORCYCLISTS)

76

DISH - dash - bash - bass - boss - bows - BOWL
(Other solutions are possible)

Solutions

77

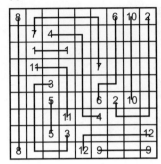

78

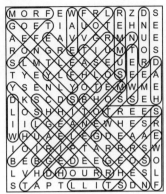

79

A	B	F	C	D	E
D	F	A	B	E	C
E	C	D	F	B	A
F	D	E	A	C	B
C	A	B	E	F	D
B	E	C	D	A	F

80

4	6	1	8	9	7	5	2	3
2	7	8	5	3	4	9	1	6
9	3	5	1	6	2	8	4	7
6	9	3	4	2	1	7	5	8
5	8	2	6	7	9	1	3	4
1	4	7	3	5	8	6	9	2
8	5	4	2	1	6	3	7	9
3	2	9	7	8	5	4	6	1
7	1	6	9	4	3	2	8	5

81

S	E	N	S	I	T	I	V	E		E		C		A
H			O		R		E		A	P	P	L	E	S
A	D	J	U	T	A	N	T	S		I		A		P
K			T		N			C	A	T	A	R	R	H
E	X	C	H	E	Q	U	E	R		O		I		Y
N			E		U		E	L	M		O		X	
		F	O	R	C	I	B	L	E		E	N	N	U	I
E			L		Y		S		O		A			
P	O	L	Y	P		P	E	D	A	N	T	I	C	
I		O		E	R	A		R		O			O	
L		Z		R		W	I	N	D	P	R	O	O	F
E	X	E	C	U	T	E		O		I			F	
P		N		S		R	A	I	N	C	O	A	T	S
S	I	G	N	A	L		I		I		U		E	
Y		E		L		B	L	A	C	K	S	P	O	T

82

5

151

Solutions

83

MAPLE · DEAL · HAZEL · ASH · ROSEWOOD · BEECH · SYCAMORE · YEW · ALDER · EUCALYPTUS · GRANADILLA · OLIVE · ELM · BRIAR · FIR

(Tree-name crossword solution — LARCH, ROSEWOOD, MAHOGANY, GRANADILLA, etc.)

84

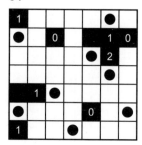

85

2	1	4	3	5
5	4	3	1	2
1	3	2	5	4
3	2	5	4	1
4	5	1	2	3

86

C

87

(Grid puzzle with numbers and black circles)

88

3	5	1	8	9	4	2	6	7
2	4	6	1	7	3	9	5	8
8	9	7	6	2	5	4	3	1
4	8	2	9	3	1	6	7	5
6	1	3	7	5	2	8	4	9
5	7	9	4	6	8	3	1	2
7	3	4	2	1	9	5	8	6
9	6	5	3	8	7	1	2	4
1	2	8	5	4	6	7	9	3

Solutions

89

90

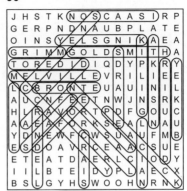

91

O	O	X	O	X	X	O	X
O	X	O	O	X	O	X	X
X	O	X	X	O	X	O	O
O	O	X	X	O	X	X	O
X	X	O	O	X	O	O	X
O	O	X	X	O	X	X	O
X	X	O	X	O	O	X	O
X	X	O	O	X	O	O	X

92

Answer: STRENGTH

93

94

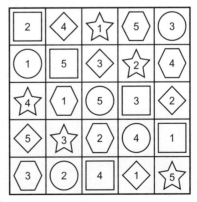

153

Solutions

95

D	E	A	B	C
A	D	B	C	E
E	B	C	A	D
B	C	D	E	A
C	A	E	D	B

97

7

96

98

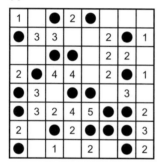

99

4	9	8	3	7	6	1	5	2
5	6	1	8	2	9	3	7	4
7	2	3	4	5	1	9	8	6
6	4	7	1	3	8	5	2	9
2	3	5	7	9	4	6	1	8
1	8	9	2	6	5	7	4	3
9	1	4	6	8	7	2	3	5
3	7	6	5	4	2	8	9	1
8	5	2	9	1	3	4	6	7

100

MEXICA ... B
CLUEDO ... H S A
H ... O ... I C T
E ... U ... N R T
SQUAREMILE ... E A L
S ... C ... T M S E E S
P Q R P E B H
A U I A E C L I
T I PARCHEESI P
SORRY I E
H L E A C T
O L L BLOKUS
TWISTER E U R
E R R
LUDO OBSESSION

101

D	E	C	B	A	C	B	E	A	D
E	B	D	A	C	E	C	A	D	B
A	E	B	C	D	B	A	D	E	C
C	B	E	D	A	D	E	C	B	A
D	A	B	C	D	E	C	B	A	E
E	D	E	A	B	C	B	A	C	D
B	C	A	D	E	B	A	D	E	C
C	D	C	E	B	A	D	E	B	A
A	C	A	B	E	D	E	C	D	B
B	A	D	E	C	A	D	B	C	E

Solutions

102

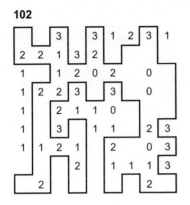

103

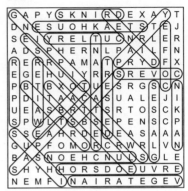

104

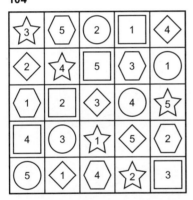

105

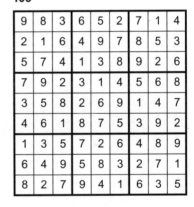

106

107

108
The nine-letter word is:
WONDERFUL

Solutions

109

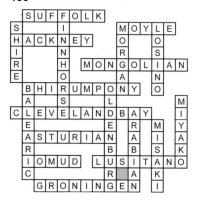

110

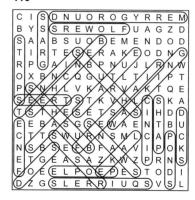

111

5	6	1	3	2	4
6	2	4	1	3	5
2	5	6	4	1	3
4	3	5	2	6	1
3	1	2	5	4	6
1	4	3	6	5	2

112

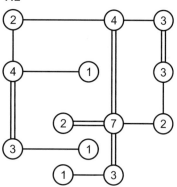

113

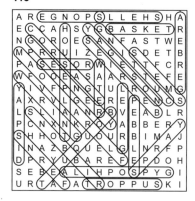

114

2	7	1	3	8	4	5	6	9
6	5	3	9	1	7	2	4	8
8	9	4	2	6	5	7	3	1
4	1	7	5	3	8	6	9	2
3	2	8	6	7	9	1	5	4
5	6	9	1	4	2	3	8	7
1	4	5	7	9	6	8	2	3
7	8	2	4	5	3	9	1	6
9	3	6	8	2	1	4	7	5

Solutions

115

116

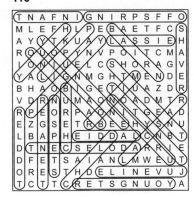

117

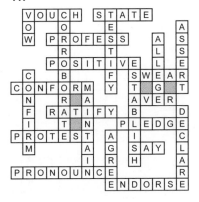

118

Answer: ALTRUISM

119

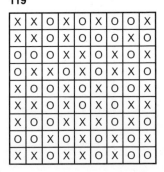

120

121

GOAT - boat - beat - peat - peas -
pegs - PIGS
(Other solutions are possible)

Solutions

122

4	6	7	8	3	2	5	1	9
9	8	1	4	7	5	2	3	6
3	2	5	1	9	6	7	4	8
2	3	6	5	8	7	4	9	1
5	7	4	9	6	1	3	8	2
1	9	8	2	4	3	6	5	7
7	1	2	3	5	8	9	6	4
8	4	3	6	2	9	1	7	5
6	5	9	7	1	4	8	2	3

123

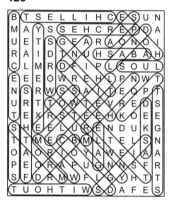

124

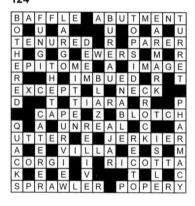

125

6	1	4	3	8	2	5	7	9
5	9	2	6	1	7	8	3	4
7	8	3	5	9	4	2	6	1
8	3	1	7	4	5	9	2	6
2	6	7	1	3	9	4	8	5
9	4	5	8	2	6	3	1	7
4	2	6	9	7	8	1	5	3
3	7	8	4	5	1	6	9	2
1	5	9	2	6	3	7	4	8

126

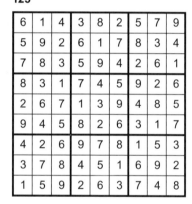

127

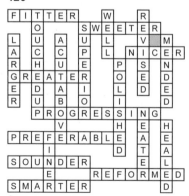

Solutions

128

129

130

5	2	7	6	1	4	3
6	7	3	4	5	2	1
1	6	2	5	3	7	4
4	1	5	3	2	6	7
3	4	1	2	7	5	6
7	5	6	1	4	3	2
2	3	4	7	6	1	5

131

8	5	9	6	7	4	2	1	3
1	7	3	2	8	9	4	6	5
6	4	2	1	5	3	9	7	8
9	8	5	3	2	6	1	4	7
2	6	1	7	4	8	3	5	9
7	3	4	9	1	5	6	8	2
3	9	7	8	6	1	5	2	4
4	2	6	5	3	7	8	9	1
5	1	8	4	9	2	7	3	6

132

3	3	1	4	6	0	1
4	2	2	3	4	3	1
0	0	6	5	6	2	3
1	0	4	4	6	4	0
0	4	2	6	1	6	4
2	2	6	3	3	0	5
5	1	2	0	5	2	5
3	1	6	5	5	1	5

133

159

Solutions

134

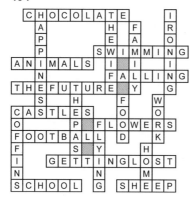

135

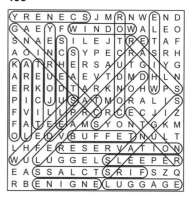

136

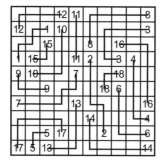

137

138

The nine-letter word is:
OBSERVING

139

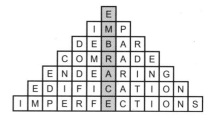

140

8	6	7	2	9	1	3	4	5
3	1	4	5	8	7	9	2	6
9	2	5	6	4	3	7	8	1
1	9	2	8	3	5	4	6	7
4	3	8	7	6	9	1	5	2
5	7	6	4	1	2	8	9	3
6	5	9	3	7	4	2	1	8
7	8	1	9	2	6	5	3	4
2	4	3	1	5	8	6	7	9